Participant Book
Catechumenate
Year B

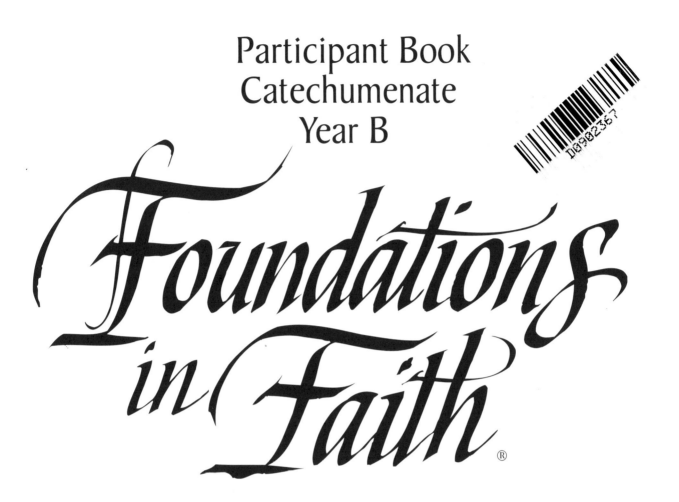

Foundations in Faith ®

Bob Duggan • Carol Gura

Rita Ferrone • Gael Gensler

Steve Lanza • Donna Steffen

Maureen A. Kelly

RCL★
Benziger®

Cincinnati, Ohio

ROMAN
MISSAL
THIRD EDITION

Contents

Nihil Obstat
Rev. Msgr. Glenn D. Gardner, J.C.D.
Censor Librorum

Imprimatur
† *Most Rev. Charles V. Grahmann*
Bishop of Dallas

July 30, 1999

The Nihil Obstat and Imprimatur are official declarations that the material reviewed is free of doctrinal or moral error. No implication is contained therein that those granting the Nihil Obstat and Imprimatur agree with the contents, opinions, or statements expressed.

Acknowledgments
Scripture excerpts are taken from the *NRSV* Copyright© 1993, 1989, by the Division of Christian Education of the National Council of the Churches of Christ in the U.S.A. Used by permission. Excerpts from the English transl. of The Roman Missal© 2011, International Committee on English in the Liturgy, Inc. (ICEL); excerpts from the English transl. of *Dedication of a Church and an Altar*© 1978, ICEL; excerpts from the English transl. of *A Book of Prayers*© 1982, ICEL. All rights reserved.

Send all inquiries to:
RCL Benziger
8805 Governor's Hill Drive, Suite 400
Cincinnati, Ohio 45249

Toll free   877-275-4725
Fax   800-688-8356

Visit us at **www.RCLBenziger.com.**

12712   ISBN 978-0-7829-0766-7

7th Printing.
November 2014.

ADVENT SEASON **3**
First Sunday of Advent. 4
Second Sunday of Advent 6
Third Sunday of Advent. 8
Fourth Sunday of Advent. 10

CHRISTMAS SEASON **13**
The Navity of the Lord (Christmas) 14
The Holy Family of Jesus, Mary, and Joseph 16
The Epiphany of the Lord 18
The Baptism of the Lord 20

LENTEN SEASON **23**
First Sunday of Lent 24
Second Sunday of Lent 26
Third Sunday of Lent 28
Fourth Sunday of Lent 30
Fifth Sunday of Lent 32
Palm Sunday of the Passion of the Lord 34

EASTER SEASON **37**
Easter Sunday 38
Second Sunday of Easter. 40
Third Sunday of Easter 42
Fourth Sunday of Easter 44
Fifth Sunday of Easter. 46
Sixth Sunday of Easter 48
Seventh Sunday of Easter 50
Pentecost Sunday. 52

ORDINARY TIME **55**
Second Sunday in Ordinary Time 56
Third Sunday in Ordinary Time. 58
Fourth Sunday in Ordinary Time. 60
Fifth Sunday in Ordinary Time 62
Sixth Sunday in Ordinary Time 64
Seventh Sunday in Ordinary Time 66
Eighth Sunday in Ordinary Time 68
Ninth Sunday in Ordinary Time. 70
Tenth Sunday in Ordinary Time 72
Eleventh Sunday in Ordinary Time 74
Twelfth Sunday in Ordinary Time 76
Thirteenth Sunday in Ordinary Time. 78
Fourteenth Sunday in Ordinary Time 80
Fifteenth Sunday in Ordinary Time 82
Sixteenth Sunday in Ordinary Time. 84
Seventeenth Sunday in Ordinary Time 86
Eighteenth Sunday in Ordinary Time 88
Nineteenth Sunday in Ordinary Time 90

Twentieth Sunday in Ordinary Time 92
Twenty-first Sunday in Ordinary Time. 94
Twenty-second Sunday in Ordinary Time 96
Twenty-third Sunday in Ordinary Time. 98
Twenty-fourth Sunday in Ordinary Time. 100
Twenty-fifth Sunday in Ordinary Time 102
Twenty-sixth Sunday in Ordinary Time 104
Twenty-seventh Sunday in Ordinary Time. 106
Twenty-eighth Sunday in Ordinary Time 108
Twenty-ninth Sunday in Ordinary Time 110
Thirtieth Sunday in Ordinary Time 112
Thirty-first Sunday in Ordinary Time † 114
Thirty-second Sunday in Ordinary Time 116
Thirty-third Sunday in Ordinary Time. 118
Thirty-fourth Sunday in Ordinary Time 120

HOLY DAYS AND FEASTS **123**
The Immaculate Conception of the Blessed Virgin Mary. . 124
Mary, the Holy Mother of God. 126
The Presentation of the Lord. 128
The Ascension of the Lord. 130
The Most Holy Trinity 132
The Most Holy Body and Blood of Christ 134
The Nativity of Saint John the Baptist 136
Saints Peter and Paul, Apostles. 138
The Transfiguration of the Lord. 140
The Assumption of the Blessed Virgin Mary 142
The Exaltation of the Holy Cross 144
All Saints 146
All Souls 148
The Dedication of the Lateran Basilica 150

Glossary of Terms **153**

Notes **157**

ADVENT SEASON

First Sunday of Advent

Scripture:

Isaiah 63:16–17, 19; 64:2–7
Psalm 80:2–3, 15–16, 18–19
1 Corinthians 1:3–9
Mark 13:33–37

Focus:

THE SECOND COMING OF CHRIST

Reflection

Directions: *Place yourself into the parable as you silently read the Gospel of Mark. You are the servants in charge. When you have finished reflecting, list in one column several of the "tasks" or "things" that God has placed under your care. In a second column, list the ways you can be more "watchful" as you await Christ's return.*

"It is like a man going on a journey, when he leaves home and puts his slaves in charge, each with his work, and commands the doorkeeper to be on the watch. Therefore, keep awake—for you do not know when the master of the house will come, in the evening, or at midnight, or at cockcrow, or at dawn, or else he may find you asleep. . . ."

Tasks, Things In My Care   *More Watchful*

Questions

1. *How have you gained some measure of calm and security in the midst of your own advents?*

2. *When have you waited for the Lord to act in your life? What was the outcome?*

Did You Know?

The traditional Advent wreath is made of evergreen branches formed into a circle with four candles, each representing the four Sundays of Advent. The importance of the Advent wreath in Christian households is derived from its rich symbolism. The circle shape of the wreath signifies eternity, with no beginning and no end. The greenery symbolizes ongoing life. The four candles around the circle are a symbol of the gradual approach of the Light of the world that will dispel the darkness.

The Church Says:

Advent, meaning "arrival," is the liturgical season during which the Church prepares to celebrate the Incarnation, the birth of the Lord. This earth-shaking event in human history began the movement that will culminate or come to fullness when Christ returns. The Second Coming refers to Christ's return to judge the living and the dead and to fulfill God's promised reign of peace and justice.

We live in the time between these two extraordinary comings. However, this is not a time of abandonment. We are not alone, for Jesus is with us, present in the Church through the power of the Holy Spirit. We are reminded this season to remain watchful in order that we might "see" Jesus in others, in creation, and in the circumstances of our lives. This time of waiting and anticipation is marked by continued conversion, in which we are to conform our lives to the image of Christ.

As we anticipate the Second Coming of Christ we are assured that life is full of possibility and promise. Therefore, hope dominates this time between Christ's comings, giving meaning and value to our lives and prompting us to transform our reality to God's plan each and every day.

For This Week:

I want to remember:

I want to put my faith into action by:

Questions to Explore

Prayer for the Week

"As the cataract of ignorance falls from off the eyesight of my soul, I realize that all this huge Creation round about me is the Word.

The hitherto quite unattended fact that these familiar fingers number ten, like an encounter with some miracle, suddenly astonishes me and the newly-opened forsythia flowers in one corner of the hedge beyond my window entrance me utterly, like seeing a model of Resurrection.

Smaller than a grain of sand in the oceanic vastness of the cosmos, I realize that this my muttering, by a mysterious grace of the Word, is no imagined thing, no mere sign, but Reality itself" (DivInsp, p. 4).

[In "The True Appearance of the Word" Ku Sang points to the presence of Christ in the everyday and ordinary events. This translation is provided by Br. Anthony of the Taizé community.]

Second Sunday of Advent

Scripture:

Isaiah 40:1–5, 9–11
Psalm 85:9–10, 11–12, 13–14
2 Peter 3:8–14
Mark 1:1–8

Focus:

CONFESSION OF SINS

Reflection

Directions: *Think back over the days since our last gathering.*

Are there words, deeds, or actions you would like to take back?

Are there words, deeds, or actions you wish you had said or done?

Are there words, deeds, or actions for which you are thankful that you said or did?

Memorable People:

John the Baptist, son of Elizabeth and Zachary, was a cousin of Jesus. John preached a baptism of repentance. He was a prophet. It was John who baptized Jesus in the Jordan River.

Father Walter Ciszek, an American Jesuit priest, volunteered to study Russian and was assigned to a mission in eastern Poland around 1938. When the Russian army invaded, he chose to go with Polish refugees being transported to labor camps in Russia, where he was arrested by the secret police in 1941. Having served several different prison sentences, totaling some 23 years, he was sent home to the United States. In his autobiography, Father Ciszek wrote, "I realized that true freedom meant nothing else than letting God operate within my soul without interference" (All Saints 536).

Did You Know?

The Council of Trent, in its teaching on confession of sins, followed St. Jerome, and used the image of a doctor of medicine who cannot help the patient because the sick person is too ashamed to show the physician the wound. Without this exposure of the wound, the doctor cannot apply the proper healing medicine. God acts as a physician to probe our hearts and by the inner voice of conscience reveals to us the first steps in our spiritual health.

The Church Says:

The call to prepare the way of the Lord, a penitential focus, is strong in the Advent liturgies. In order to prepare for the coming of the Lord one must experience conversion, confession of sins, and true repentance by following the Lord's "way." Advent points us to our Redemption in Christ, whose birth and incarnation we prepare to celebrate and whose coming again in glory we anticipate. That the gift of Redemption goes hand in hand with our acknowledgment of sin is the focus for us today. The confession of our sins points to the healing mercy of a forgiving God.

Naming, or confessing, one's sins, even from a purely human point of view, enables a person to move forward in life with a certain freedom, the freedom that comes from admitting that one has failed oneself and others. From the perspective of faith, the confession of sin is basically a proclamation of our trust in God's saving love. By acknowledging our faults and sins, we accept our responsibility and open ourselves to the healing mercy of a forgiving God. John the Baptist stands forth as a beacon, calling each believer to the admission that we are not perfect and that we need God and God's grace in a radical way, reorienting our lives. Confessing sin can thus be seen as centering ourselves and our lives in God. Turning from sin and embracing God is nothing less than conversion, which requires a truthful self-examination.

For This Week:

I want to remember:

I want to put my faith into action by:

Questions to Explore

Prayer for the Week

*"Father of Mercies and God of Consolation,
you do not wish the sinner to die
but to be converted and live.
Come to the aid of your people,
that they may turn from their sins
and live for you alone.
May we be attentive to your word, confess
our sins, receive your forgiveness, and be
always grateful for your loving kindness.
Help us to live the truth in love and grow into
the fullness of Christ, your Son, who lives
and reigns for ever and ever."
Amen.*

Fourth Sunday of Advent

Scripture:

2 Samuel 7:1–5; 8–12, 14–16
Psalm 89:2–3, 4–5, 27, 29
Romans 16:25–27
Luke 1:26–38

Focus:

INCARNATION

Reflection

Directions: *Spend some time thinking about the images from Luke's Gospel listed below. You may find it helpful to place yourself into the scene of the Annunciation. Next to the Gospel quote, name some ways in which this image or phrase has meaning for your life.*

"Greetings, favored one!" (Luke 1:28)

"The Lord is with you." (Luke 1:28)

"She was much perplexed by his words and pondered what sort of greeting this might be." (Luke 1:29)

"You have found favor with God." (Luke 1:30)

"You will conceive in your womb and bear a son . . . he will be called the Son of the Most High." (Luke 1:31–32)

"How can this be since I am a virgin?" (Luke 1:34)

"The power of the Most High will overshadow you." (Luke 1:35)

"For nothing will be impossible with God." (Luke 1:37)

"Let it be done with me according to your word." (Luke 1:38)

Questions

1. What do you find consoling about this passage? Confusing?

2. How can you respond to this mystery of Jesus, born in human flesh of the virgin Mary?

Did You Know?

Artifacts made by human hands can also communicate to us something of that divine glory. The images found in liturgical texts and the depictions of Christian artwork—such as icons, statues, and religious paintings—not only edify our faith but also offer a way to appreciate and contemplate the glory of God. Saint John of Damascus (d. 749) wrote: "I do not worship matter. I worship the Creator of matter who became matter for my sake, who willed to take his abode in matter, and who through matter wrought my salvation" (NDictSacr, 67). Art historian Marchita B. Mauck reflects: "Icons have such an extraordinary role because their very existence lies in the christological controversies of early centuries. Icons of Christ and the Virgin witness to the dogma of the incarnation in affirming that God became fully human and that human beings will become divine. That is the economy of God's salvation" (NDictSacr, 67).

The Church Says:

The center of our faith is the Incarnation because the Affirmation that the eternal Word of God became flesh affects our whole understanding of Christ. The Incarnation, that is, that the Word came down from Heaven and by the power of the Holy Spirit was born of the virgin Mary and became man, is the culmination of God's promise to send a redeemer, a Messiah, to save all people. There are four reasons that make the Incarnation apparent to the eyes of faith. (1) The Word became flesh to save us by reconciling us to God, healing the breach between God and humanity. (2) In the Incarnation we discover the depths of God's love for us. (3) Jesus' coming to dwell among us taught us how to live the holiness of life, rooted in the new Law of Love. (4) Through the Incarnation we can share in the divine nature, that is, by Baptism we are incorporated into the mystery of Christ and given a share in the divine nature.

For This Week:

I want to remember:

I want to put my faith into action by:

Questions to Explore

Prayer for the Week

Respond to God's words in the scriptures
from the Fourth Sunday of Advent by praying
after each phrase:
Let us sing the goodness of the Lord.

I have been with you since the beginning of time . . .
I will fix a place for my people . . .
I have made a covenant with my chosen one . . .
I will maintain my kindness toward you . . .
*My covenant with you stands firm and lasts forever
. . .*
I will strengthen you in the gospel . . .
To you I reveal the mystery hidden for many ages . . .
Rejoice, O highly favored Daughters and Sons . . .

CHRISTMAS SEASON

The Nativity of the Lord (Christmas), Mass during the Day

Scripture:

Isaiah 52:7–10
Psalm 98:1, 2–3, 3–4, 5–6
Hebrews 1:1–6
John 1:1–18

Focus:

THE INCARNATION

Reflection

Directions: The images from today's Scriptures help us to unfold the depths of the Incarnation. Incarnation means that by Jesus' birth into the human situation, God has revealed the depths of divine love to us. This is the source of our comfort and Redemption. Use the space below to write your reaction to some of the images from today's Scripture. In your writing, note your feelings and the meaning of the images and phrases as you try to grapple with the mystery of the Incarnation.

At the beginning of creation, the Word, with God, brought all things into being.

Jesus, Son of God, the Word, became flesh, dwelt among us.

This Word was God, a light that shines in the darkness.

The Word empowered us to become children of God.

Of his fullness we have all had a share—love following upon love.

The Word is God's self-Revelation.

The Word made flesh, died for our sins and rose from the dead.

The glory of the Risen Jesus, who now sits at the right hand of the Father.

Questions

1. *What do these images reveal to you about the nature of God?*

2. *What is the Good News of this solemnity for you?*

3. *What is the Good News of the Incarnation for the world?*

Memorable People:

On December 26 the Church celebrates the feast of Saint Stephen, the first martyr. A martyr is someone who is willing to die for his or her belief in God. Stephen, a deacon in the early Church, proclaimed the Good News of God's coming to Earth to redeem humankind and for this was stoned to death. Later, during this same week, the Church remembers the young children slaughtered by Herod, who jealously feared the newborn king and Messiah would usurp his powers. These Holy Innocents are remembered on December 28.

Did You Know?

The Solemnity of Christmas coincides with the ancient pagan festival of lights, during which ancient tribes gathered around bonfires to ward off the long darkness with firelight. Jesus is the Light of the world, dispelling all darkness.

The Church Says:

Christmas is a celebration of the Incarnation. The eternal Word of God became flesh in Jesus' birth. God's love is not distant but draws us into God's family as children and heirs to heaven. We did not merit the Incarnation, nor can we earn God's immanent presence. Rather, in Jesus we see and experience the love of God poured upon us in radiant light. Through the Incarnation, God lifts up all things to God's very self, restores unity to all of creation, and leads us from exile to the Kingdom of Heaven. Thus, in the Word made flesh, we are reconciled to God and offered the gift of Salvation.

For This Week:

I want to remember:

I want to put my faith into action by:

Questions to Explore

Prayer for the Week

Word of God, Son of God, born among humankind,
We rejoice this day,
For you have revealed to us and to all of creation
The marvelous light of your glory,
The farthest reaches of your love,
The power of your gift of reconciliation.
Draw us ever closer to your heart
That we might fathom the depths
of your love,
Appreciate the freedom of your Redemption
And someday share in the glory
of your heavenly kingdom.
With all the ends of the earth
We rejoice and proclaim your coming,
your Salvation,
your enduring love.
Amen.

Epiphany of the Lord

Scripture:

Isaiah 60:1–6
Psalm 72:1–2, 7–8, 10–11, 12–13
Ephesians 3:2–3, 5–6
Matthew 2:1–12

Focus:

UNIVERSAL OFFER OF SALVATION

Reflection

Directions: *Read and reflect on this legend about the Magi. When you have finished, write your reaction, including your feelings, insights, and revelations, in the space provided.*

The legend is that the three Magi were of different ages. The elder Magi entered the stable alone and found an older man with whom he shared the wisdom he had gained in life. The middle-aged man then entered the stable and found a middle-aged person with whom he shared his struggles and disappointments in life and asked the questions on his mind. The younger Magi entered the stable and found a young man with whom he shared his hopes, dreams, and visions of life. Then, when the three entered the stable together, they found the infant, Jesus.

Questions

1. *What do you seek as you enter the stable in your quest for Jesus?*

2. *How has Christ illuminated your life on your journey in faith toward initiation?*

3. *In what ways are you being challenged to bring the light of Christ into the world?*

Memorable People:

The feast of Saint Elizabeth Ann Seton, the first American-born Saint, 1774–1821, is on January 4, near the Solemnity of the Epiphany. Elizabeth, the mother of five children, converted to Catholicism when she was widowed and began the first American religious society, the Sisters of Charity of St. Joseph. Elizabeth shed the light of Christ in the New World by opening schools for the poor. She is credited with beginning Catholic education in the United States. She was canonized a Saint on September 14, 1975.

Did You Know?

Gloriously decorated and adorned Christmas trees are a relatively modern practice derived from medieval mystery plays which depicted the tree of paradise and the Christmas light of candles symbolizing Christ, light of the whole world. The tree is usually set up just before Christmas and remains in its prominent place until after this Solemnity of the Epiphany. The prayer which the Church offers in blessing the Christmas tree includes references to the joy of this season but also looks forward to the Lenten and Easter seasons when the Death and Resurrection of Jesus are celebrated. One form of the Christmas tree blessing exults, "Holy Lord, we come with joy to celebrate the birth of your Son, who rescued us from the darkness of sin by making the cross a tree of life and light. May this tree, arrayed in splendor, remind us of the life-giving cross of Christ, that we may always rejoice in the new life that shines in our hearts."

The Church Says:

Epiphany, a great feast celebrated from the earliest Christian centuries, occupies a place of even greater prominence than Christmas among the Eastern Churches. Christmas celebrates the Incarnation—God took on human flesh in Jesus. Epiphany celebrates the Revelation of this great cosmic event to the whole world. This feast underscores the Revelation of God's saving love in Jesus. This action of God stretches beyond the Israelites to embrace the Gentiles. The radiant dawning of light dominating the first reading from Isaiah and the light of the star found in Matthew's Gospel indicates the light of Christ covers and illuminates all peoples, for all times.

The Church by her very nature is universal and inclusive. The mission of the Church is to invite all people to share in the banquet of God's love. At the Second Vatican Council, the bishops of the world addressed the Church's relationship with other Christians and non-Christians in the document known as *Lumen gentium* (Light of the Nations). This document presents the Church's self-understanding as a sign and instrument of communion with God and of unity among all people. The Church stands at the service of Jesus' universal and reconciling mission to the world. Thus, the Church is called to give witness and to bring about this unity and reconciliation in the world.

For This Week:

I want to remember:

I want to put my faith into action by:

Questions to Explore

Prayer for the Week

*Loving and gracious God,
Epiphany celebrates that
your Revelation to all people of faith
in the Word
was made flesh in Jesus.
Your light is strong!
Your love is near!
Keep our hearts open to the guidance of
this marvelous light
as we seek and search for you.
Enlighten our minds and hearts
that we might know you and
follow your ways.
Let our light shine forth
as we share your Son Jesus
with our brothers and sisters
throughout the world. Amen.*

Baptism of the Lord

Scripture:

Isaiah 55:1–11
Isaiah 12:2–3, 4bcd, 5–6
1 John 5:1–9
Mark 1:7–11

THE HOLY SPIRIT

Reflection

1. *John the Baptist said he baptizes with water, while Jesus will baptize with the Holy Spirit. When Jesus was baptized, the Spirit descended upon him. What do you think is the significance of the Spirit coming upon Jesus, and us, at Baptism? In what ways do you sense the Spirit impacts us?*

2. *The Spirit gifts us in many ways. The Gifts of the Spirit named in Scripture and honored in Catholic tradition are listed below. Catholic tradition also claims that the Spirit's presence is known by the Fruits of the Spirit named in Galatians 5:25 and cited below.*

GIFTS OF THE SPIRIT	FRUITS OF THE SPIRIT	
wisdom	*love*	*kindness*
understanding	*joy*	*goodness*
counsel	*peace*	*faithfulness*
fortitude	*patience*	*gentleness*
knowledge	*self-control*	
piety		
fear (awe) of the Lord		

Consider these various Gifts and Fruits of the Spirit. Circle the ones you find present in you. Give examples of situations where you find their presence. Put a box around the ones you particularly need or desire to come alive in you at this time. Why did you choose these?

Quotable Quotes:

Twelfth-century abbess and mystic, Hildegard of Bingen, wrote the following antiphon for the Holy Spirit: The spirit of God is a life that bestows life, root of the world tree and wind in its boughs. Scrubbing out sins, she rubs oil into wounds. She is glistening life, alluring all praise, all-awakening, all-resurrecting.

(Source: Symphonia, translated and edited by Barbara Newman, Ithaca: Cornell University Press, 1988, p. 141)

Did You Know?

Since the New Testament reports that the Spirit descended upon Jesus as a dove (Mark 1:10), artists have depicted the Holy Spirit as a dove. This dove symbol is common in catacombs and on early Christian sarcophagi (burial containers). Other images of the Spirit include wind and fire from the experience of the Spirit at Pentecost (Acts 2:2–4).

The Church Says:

The Holy Spirit, the Third Person of the Trinity, is equal to the Father and the Son, and is thus worshiped and glorified. Though there are Three Persons, there is only One God. The activity of the Holy Spirit is revealed in the many names for the Spirit: Spirit of God, Breath of God, Advocate, Guide, Consoler, and Paraclete who quickens our faith.

The Holy Spirit has acted throughout history. The Spirit was present at the time of creation as the wind hovered over the waters of chaos, and as God breathed life into the clay of the ground, forming a human person. The Spirit spoke through the prophets. The Spirit overshadowed Mary and brought about the incarnation. Jesus came to bring forth God's reign. After his Death, Resurrection, and Ascension, the continuation of this mission is handed over to the Church, empowered by the constant presence of the Spirit. Through the Spirit the baptized share in the mission of Christ.

The Spirit bestows gifts upon the People of God to bring about God's reign in the world. The Spirit propels us beyond human limitations through new life and energy. The Spirit, at times symbolized by fire or wind, acts through us in amazing, surprising, and unpredictable ways. Challenging our comfortable existence, the Spirit transforms us to live in God's freedom, strength, and power. Those who have eyes to see recognize the continuous activity of the Spirit.

For This Week:

I want to remember:

I want to put my faith into action by:

Questions to Explore

Prayer for the Week

Gracious Spirit of God,
Come, breathe your life in me
that I may dwell in your heart.
Come, set my heart ablaze with your love
that I may bear your presence to others.
Come, awaken my spirit
that I may know your action in my life.
Come, challenge my limited self
that I may grow beyond my comfort.
Come, fill me through the waters of Baptism
that I may help to bring about your reign.
Come, renew and refresh all your people,
that your world may be recreated.
Amen.

LENTEN SEASON

First Sunday of Lent

Scripture:

Genesis 9:8–15
Psalm 25:4–5, 6–7, 8–9
1 Peter 3:18–22
Mark 1:12–15

Focus:

BAPTISMAL COVENANT

Reflection

Directions: *Spend time thinking about the significance of the images from today's Scriptures in your own life. Ask yourself: When have I experienced God's presence in a time like that of Noah or of Jesus? Then focus on one of these experiences and describe the circumstances and how God was present for you, even if you did not realize God's faithfulness at the time.*

NOAH
Destructive flood (time when everything seemed lost or in chaos)
Ark of safety (ways in which you survived)
Rainbow of God's promise (God's care became obvious)

JESUS
Forty days of wilderness (time of trial when you discovered your identity)
Wild beasts (what appeared to be harmful proved not to destroy you)
Ministering angels (those who made God's care real for you during this time of trial)

Questions

1. *What does the image of God's reign mean for you?*

2. *How can you repent and believe more consciously this Lent?*

3. *What does Baptism mean to you in the light of these Scriptures?*

Quotable Quote:

> *God is love, and those who abide in love abide in God, and God abides in them. . . .*
> *We love because he first loved us. (1 John 4:16, 19)*

The Church Says:

The original blessing and promise of creation was renewed by God in the Covenant with Noah and later in the Covenants between God and Abraham and between God and Moses at Mt. Sinai. God initiates the Covenant, reaching out in love to humankind and all of creation. In Baptism we enter into a committed relationship with God in Christ. This Covenant of Baptism is a result of God's initiative of grace, since God first chooses to gift us.The Covenant of God is not based on our human qualifications because human infidelity or limitations cannot compromise God's love.

In Baptism we are plunged into the waters, that is, we are immersed into Christ's Death and made a new creation. Our response to God's initiative of love is obedience, "to hear" and heed God's call. Through Baptism we "put on Christ," that is, we conform to the image of Christ with the support of the entire Church community. In Baptism we are challenged to live for others, to join in the mission of Christ, and to proclaim our faith to the world.

For This Week:

I want to remember:

I want to put my faith into action by:

Questions to Explore

Prayer for the Week

Creator God, you offered a rainbow as a sign of your covenant, promising never again to destroy your creation by the waters of the flood. These floodwaters, a sign of purification and death, remind us of the baptismal waters by which we are plunged deeper into the mystery of your pledge of faithful love, O God. Cleanse our hearts and purify our attitudes during these forty days of Lent. Create a newness in our hearts that we might clothe ourselves in Christ and heed your call to renew the face of the earth. Grant us the grace to come to know you through Jesus our Savior. Pour out your living waters as a sign of your overflowing grace. Amen.

Second Sunday of Lent

Scripture:

Genesis 22:1–2, 9a, 10–13, 15–18
Psalm 116:10, 15, 16–17, 18–19
Romans 8:31b–34
Mark 9:2–10

Focus:

SACRIFICE

Questions

1. *Name the scenes described in today's readings, and then describe the feelings each of these scenes evokes within you.*

2. *Does any one of the scenes offer you comfort? If yes, in what way?*

3. *Does any one of the scenes offer a challenge or disturb you in some way? If yes, in what way?*

4. *What might be the message today of each of these readings for your life?*

Did You Know?

The elements of sacrifice are an object offered, someone to make the offering, and the consummation, or complete burning, of the offering. In the passage from Genesis the elements of sacrifice are an object offered: Isaac, who carries the wood for the sacrifice; someone to make the offering: Abraham; the consummation: the ram that was substituted for Isaac was burned as an offering to God.

The elements of Jesus as sacrifice are the one offered: Jesus, who also carries the wood for the sacrifice; someone to make the offering: Jesus offers himself; consummation: Jesus dies on the Cross as ransom for our sins and is raised from the dead in three days.

The elements of the sacrifice of the Mass are the one offered: Jesus in the bread and wine; the one who offers the sacrifice: Jesus, who acts in and through the priest; consummation: the Body and Blood of Jesus are consumed by those present, in Holy Communion. Note: some of the consecrated hosts are reserved for the sick, the homebound, the dying.

The Church Says:

The Christian tradition has seen in Abraham's sacrifice of Isaac a foreshadowing of God's offering Jesus up to a sacrificial death. The reading from Romans relates the justification of sinful humanity to God's overwhelming love shown in the sacrifice of his Son, Jesus. Thus, the sacrifice prefigured by Abraham's willingness to sacrifice his son is perfectly realized in Jesus Christ, who freely offers himself to the Father as a ransom for our sins. Through his sacrifice on the Cross Jesus establishes in his blood the new and eternal Covenant.

The Eucharist makes present this once-for-all sacrifice of Christ who died as ransom for our sins. The Mass is sometimes called the Holy Sacrifice, meaning the holy sacrifice of Jesus Christ.

The Eucharist is also the sacrifice of the Body of believers, the Church. In celebrating this sacramental action, the Body is united to the Head, that is, the Church herself is being offered through Christ. The lives of the household of the faithful, whole and entire, are offered to the Father through the Son and in the Spirit. All of our praise, sufferings, difficulties, prayer, and good works are united with Christ in his own total offering.

For This Week:

I want to remember:

I want to put my faith into action by:

Questions to Explore	Prayer for the Week

From the *Roman Missal*, The Preparation of the Gifts

Blessed are you, Lord God of all creation,
for through your goodness we have received
the bread we offer you:
fruit of the earth and work of human hands,
it will become for us the bread of life.

. . . for through your goodness we have received
the wine we offer you:
fruit of the vine and work of human hands,
it will become our spiritual drink.

May the Lord accept the sacrifice at your hands
for the praise and glory of his name,
for our good
and the good of all his holy Church.

Third Sunday of Lent

Scripture:

Exodus 20:1–17, or 20:1–3, 7–8, 12–17
Psalm 19:8, 9, 10, 11
1 Corinthians 1:22–25
John 2:13–25

Focus:

THE TEN COMMANDMENTS

Reflection

The Ten Commandments, taken from Exodus 20:1-17 and Deuteronomy 5:6-21, are:

1. *I am the LORD your God: you shall not have strange gods before me.*

2. *You shall not take the name of the LORD your God in vain.*

3. *Remember to keep holy the LORD's Day.*

4. *Honor your father and your mother.*

5. *You shall not kill.*

6. *You shall not commit adultery.*

7. *You shall not steal.*

8. *You shall not bear false witness against your neighbor.*

9. *You shall not covet your neighbor's wife.*

10. *You shall not covet your neighbor's goods.*

Directions: *Circle the Commandments that have been the most difficult for you in the past. Place an "x" next to the Commandment that is presenting the greatest challenge to you now. What do you sense is the new life that God is inviting you to through the Commandment(s) you marked?*

Memorable People:

In 1954 Bernard Haring wrote *The Law of Christ*, a breakthrough book that moved modern Catholic moral theology from a focus on a legalistic understanding of the Ten Commandments to one that looked toward the goal and spirit of the Commandments. Rather than simply stating minimum requirements, the Commandments are fulfilled in an attitude of love and life described by Jesus in the Beatitudes.

Did You Know?

Michelangelo (d. 1564) sculpted the figure of Moses for the tomb of Pope Julius II, which is found in the church of St. Peter in Chains in Rome. In this sculpture Moses is seated, holding the tablets of the Law, the Ten Commandments. Protruding from Moses' head are two horns, usually understood to symbolize wisdom. Moses' immense vitality seems to show God's Law as true wisdom. Various depictions of Moses often include him holding two tablets, the Law God gave him on Mt. Sinai.

The Church Says:

The Ten Commandments stand at the heart of God's Covenant with the Israelites at the time of Moses. Obedience to the Commandments embodied the Israelites' faithful response to the God who "brought you out of the land of Egypt." The God who established a covenant of love, the God who freed Israel, now gives Israel a guideline to what life is like in relationship with God. These statements are presented as direct commands forbidding offenses against God, whereas other codes in the Hebrew Scriptures appear as crimes against people.

In the Commandments God clearly indicates that there is only one God, the creator God of everything. This God is to be the center of our lives and nothing less. Each of the Commandments has broader understandings than their explicit statement. For example, the command not to kill may include other lesser offenses such as physically harming another. When the spirit of the Commandment is applied to the Law, a fuller basis for Christian morality is expressed.

Providing a sound moral basis for Christian life, the Ten Commandments find their fullest expression in the life and teaching of Christ. In the Beatitudes, found in the Gospel of Luke and in the Sermon on the Mount in Matthew (paralleling God's giving the Commandments to Moses on Mt. Sinai), Jesus unfolds a fuller expression of what it means to live as part of God's reign. Jesus goes beyond any minimal way of living the Commandments when he declares that the greatest Commandment is to love God and to love our neighbor as we love ourselves. Universal love truly is the fulfillment of the Ten Commandments.

For This Week:

I want to remember:

I want to put my faith into action by:

Questions to Explore

Prayer for the Week

Loving and gracious God,
your Law is good and refreshes my soul.
Your ways are trustworthy
and give wisdom to my simple heart.
Your words are more precious than gold,
your truths sweeter than honey.
Teach my humble heart your ways.

Open my eyes to your truths.

Give me a generous spirit,
and a willingness to change.
Help me to let go of old hurts and fears
that keep me from living
more fully in your love.
Amen.

Fourth Sunday of Lent

Scripture:

2 Chronicles 36:14–16, 19–23
Psalm 137:1–2, 3, 4–5, 6
Ephesians 2:4–10
John 3:14–21

Focus:

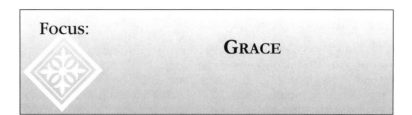

GRACE

Reflection

Directions: *Think about your past. Jot down some key moments in the space provided. Recall these moments and determine how God's incredible love was present throughout your history. With the eyes of faith, write your story of God's gift of saving love, your personal story of God's favor.*

Questions

1. *From the presentation on grace and your life experience, how would you describe grace?*

2. *What effects has God's grace had in your life?*

3. *How are you going to respond to this incredible God of love in word and deed? Be specific!*

Quotable Quote:

"For God so loved the world that he gave his only Son, so that everyone who believes in him may not perish but may have eternal life." (John 3: 16)

Memorable People:

Twelfth-century mystic Hildegard of Bingen described our response to God's love: The true and ardent lamp of Charity was lighted when God so loved humanity that for its love [God] sent His Only-Begotten to take a human body. . . . And so [God] inflamed [humankind] with Charity that they might faithfully assist all the needs, and this virtue is clothed with the tunic of God's sweetness that she may shine upon all people with true light for their devotion, use and profit.

The Church Says:

Grace encompasses a wealth of meaning, a form of God's presence, God's gift to us. Grace is undeserved, cannot be earned, and flows from God. Grace results in our participation in the life of God, through Jesus, whose Death and Resurrection made us adopted sons and daughters of God, sharing in God's own divine nature, and heirs of eternal life.

In Baptism we are made holy—sanctified—making us a new person, a new creation. We call this sanctifying, or habitual, grace, that is, the grace of Baptism gifts us to live out this new life. Actual grace describes God's continual help throughout our lives. Although we make these distinctions, the important fact is that grace demonstrates the tremendous love of God for us. Through God's Covenant with us, many graces, or gifts, are poured into our lives empowering us to attain and grow in union with God. We are free to respond to God's grace by leading a life of good deeds or to reject the gifts God offers.

For This Week:

I want to remember:

I want to put my faith into action by:

Questions to Explore

Prayer for the Week

God, you are rich in mercy,
giving us your only Son,
who became like us in everything but sin.
Your great love for humankind
extends beyond all our imaginings,
for you gifted us with Salvation,
freely offered in lifting Jesus on the Cross
and lifting him to your right hand in glory.
We cannot earn or merit this saving grace;
we can only stand in awe and silence at
your goodness!
Strengthen and inspire us to respond
to your unbelievable love in the goodness
that we do in word and deed.
Amen.

Fifth Sunday of Lent

Scripture:

Jeremiah 31:31–34
Psalm 51:3–4, 12–13, 14–15
Hebrews 5:7–9
John 12:20–33

Focus:

CHRISTIAN PRAYER

Questions

1. *When Jeremiah says that the Lord will put the law within them and write it on their hearts, what sort of things do you think the Lord wrote?*

2. *What would you want the Lord to write on your heart? Why?*

Did You Know?

Catholic postures for prayer are varied: kneeling indicates penance for sinfulness; standing indicates readiness for Christian work in the world on behalf of God's kingdom; and prostration, total humility before the power of God. Arms outstretched with palms open indicate we are open to the gift of God's grace. This posture originated with our Jewish forebears. Hands folded together dates from medieval times when a subject pledged allegiance to a king or overlord (the king placed his hands around the folded hands of his subject.)

The Church Says:

The practice of prayer is the habit of being aware of the abiding presence of God, whom we acknowledge as Father, Son, and Spirit. It is the attempt to direct one's whole self to the awareness of this presence, to be in communion with the Trinity. This communion is always possible for believers, because we have been united with Christ in the Sacrament of Baptism, the gateway to life in the Trinity. Prayer, which can be vocal or unspoken, is always Christian because we are united with the Father and the Spirit through Christ our mediator. Because our prayer is as boundless as Christ's love, it can be extended throughout the Church, his Body, and to all the world.

We believe that prayer issues not from the mouth but from the very core of the human person. In the First Reading, Jeremiah saw the breakdown of the Covenant and the disastrous consequences arising from unresponsive hearts. The heart of the person who prays is not the physical heart but the deepest, most hidden core, beyond our reason and psychic drives, where human decisions are formed, where judgments are made leading to the way of life or to the way of death.

The heart is the meeting place, the sacred place of encounter between God and the person. This is because, as creatures made in the image of God, we were created to be in relationships, just as it is God's nature to be in relationship—Father, Son, and Spirit. In the very depth of our being is found the place of covenant between us creatures and the Creator who has fashioned us in love and for love in order to be in relationship with God's very self.

For This Week:

I want to remember:

I want to put my faith into action by:

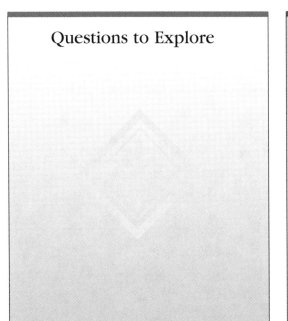

Questions to Explore

Prayer for the Week

*Loving and gentle God, be praised
for the gift of life and of all creation.*

*You have created me in your image
and likeness.*

*Probe my heart and know my desire to
deepen my love for you.*

*Create in me a longing to bring my thoughts,
words, and deeds into harmony with your
Covenant established by Jesus Christ,
who died that I might be free.*

Amen.

Palm Sunday of the Passion of the Lord

Scripture:

(Procession) Mark 11:1–10 or John 12:12–16
Isaiah 50:4–7
Psalm 22:8–9, 17–18, 19–20, 23–24
Philippians 2:6–11
Matthew 26:14–27:66
[or (short form) 27:11–54]

Focus:

THE GIFT OF PERSERVERANCE

Reflection

Directions: *Contemplate the significance of these poetic images of the Suffering Servant and Jesus taken from the first two readings of today's liturgy. Think about your own life, your struggles and sufferings. In the third column indicate how you live as a follower of Christ by persevering in faithfulness to God.*

ISAIAH	PHILIPPIANS	YOUR LIFE
The Suffering Servant speaks to the weary a rousing word	*Jesus' name is above all others*	
I have not rebelled	*Jesus was obedient unto death*	
I have not turned back	*Jesus took the form of a slave*	
I did not shield my face	*Christ did not grasp at equality with God*	
God is my help	*Christ humbled himself*	
I shall not be put to shame	*Every tongue confesses that Jesus Christ is Lord*	

Questions

The attitude of Christ we are exhorted to embody as his followers includes the following qualities: perseverance, humility, trust in God, hope, and self-emptying. You may wish to add additional qualities. Recall a time of suffering in your own life. When you are experiencing suffering, which of these qualities are the most difficult for you to embody? What helps you to persevere in your faithfulness to God?

Memorable People:

Saint Ignatius (d. 107), the third bishop of Antioch, persevered in faith even as he was martyred by wild beasts in Rome. He wrote: "Do not stand in the way of my coming to life. . . . Let me imitate the Passion of my God" (Early Christian Fathers, New York: Macmillian Company, 1970, p. 105–6).

Saint Maximilian Kolbe, a priest who gave his life in exchange for a fellow prisoner's in Auschwitz, a concentration camp, during World War II, is a modern example of perseverance in Christ. His feast day is August 14.

Did You Know?

Catholics weave the palm branches from today's liturgy into crosses and place them, or entire palm branches, in their homes to be visible signs of our desire to persevere with Christ in suffering.

The Church Says:

The liturgy for Palm Sunday of the Passion of the Lord begins with an acknowledgment of Jesus as heir to David's throne in his triumphal entry into Jerusalem. The proclamation of Isaiah's description of the Suffering Servant, of the ancient Christian hymn in Philippians expressing Christ's total self-emptying for us, and of the Passion narrative from Mark's Gospel moves us into the mystery of Jesus' Death. Thus, the liturgical color red is used to bring to mind Jesus' martyrdom. In this total gift of self in death God exalted Christ.

In Christ we are given the example of one who lived his life in total perseverance. Even the threat of death could not lure Jesus away from total faithfulness to God. As followers of Christ, we, too, are exhorted to live our lives in perseverance, no matter what struggles or sufferings meet us in life.

Catholics know that perseverance involves the gift of God's grace as well as our response to this gift. Perseverance is founded on an utter trust in God's love that will guide us on right paths and bring about our ultimate good. The gift of perseverance keeps our hearts focused on our final goal, union with God in Christ through the Spirit. The virtue of hope, which trusts that God will save people in spite of every difficulty, is a close counterpart of perseverance.

For This Week:

I want to remember:

I want to put my faith into action by:

Questions to Explore

 ### Prayer for the Week

Lord Jesus Christ,
you triumphantly rode into Jerusalem,
and later were killed there.
May our hearts learn from you
to trust in God in all things,
to never give up on the power of love,
to be willing to sacrifice ourselves
to bring about God's ways,
and to live in humility all our lives.
Give us the gift of perseverance
to give ourselves totally
in faithfulness to God,
no matter what struggles or sufferings
meet us in life.
We pray in the name of Jesus.
Amen.

EASTER SEASON

Easter Sunday

Scripture:

Acts 10:34, 37–43
Psalm 118:1–2, 16–17, 22–23
Colossians 3:1–4
    or 1 Corinthians 5:6–8
John 20:1–9

Focus:

"[HE] ROSE AGAIN ON THE THIRD DAY, IN ACCORDANCE WITH THE SCRIPTURES . . ."

Reflection

Directions: Think about your experiences of Easter. In the space below, describe your earliest understanding of the meaning of Easter and compare it to your understanding today. Name some people and events that have influenced your understanding.

Questions

1. *Why is the Resurrection of Jesus such Good News?*

2. *What does it mean for you to say, "I believe that Jesus has truly risen"?*

3. *What does the Resurrection mean in your life?*

Did You Know?

In pre-Christian times, the egg became a symbol of spring and fertility—something living comes forth from a seemingly "dead" shell. The custom of decorating special Easter eggs evolved soon after Christianity found a foothold in northern Europe and Asia. Eggs were included in the Lenten fast and for this reason they were also associated with the Easter season. Easter eggs were mostly colored with vegetable dyes. The Syrians and Greeks dyed the eggs crimson to suggest the Blood of Christ. Slavic Easter eggs are lavishly and painstakingly decorated. Armenian Easter eggs are decorated with hand-painted religious pictures or scenes. In Germany, Easter eggs are hung from trees and bushes.

The Church Says:

The unconditional and overwhelming love of God for us, made visible in the birth of his only Son, does not disappear and fade with the Death of Jesus on the Cross. God's love transcends the tomb by raising Jesus from death. The Resurrection of Jesus is a passing over from death into a new life, a new existence. By his Resurrection, Jesus breaks the chains of sin and death that hold the human race captive. Just as God took on our humanity in the Incarnation, the birth of Jesus, so too the Resurrection of Jesus was accomplished in a real human body.

Jesus' Resurrection is an actual historical event and not a psychological or spiritual experience of the disciples. Those first disciples witnessed something totally unexpected and surprising when they found the empty tomb. Later, as they experienced the Risen Lord eating and drinking in their presence, they gradually understood that he had truly risen. In understanding this, they were compelled by the Holy Spirit to proclaim the Good News of the Resurrection, even to the point of being martyred (put to death) for their faith. We, too, are transformed by the power of the Resurrection, particularly through the Sacraments of Baptism and the Eucharist.

For This Week:

I want to remember:

I want to put my faith into action by:

Questions to Explore

Prayer for the Week

Christians, to the Paschal Victim
Offer your thankful praises!
A Lamb the sheep redeems; Christ, who only is sinless,
Reconciles sinners to the Father.
Death and life have contended in that combat
stupendous:
The Prince of Life, who died, reigns immortal.
Speak Mary, declaring
What you saw, wayfaring.
"The tomb of Christ, who is living,
The glory of Jesus' resurrection;
"Bright angels attesting,
The shroud and napkin resting.
"Yes, Christ my hope is arisen:
To Galilee he goes before you."
Christ indeed from death is risen, our new life
obtaining.
Have mercy, victor King, ever reigning!
Amen.Alleluia.
(Sequence for Easter Sunday)

Second Sunday of Easter

Scripture:

Acts 4:32–35
Psalm 118:2–4, 13–15, 22–24
1 John 5:1–6
John 20:19–31

Focus:
THE CHALLENGE OF PEACE

Reflection

Directions: *Take some time to think about the meaning of Jesus' greeting, Shalom: "Peace be with you. As the Father has sent me, so I send you." Harmony with all people and with all creation is a sign of the reign of God—present, but not yet fulfilled. As one sent into the world to bring about this reign, empowered by the Holy Spirit, what implications does this greeting bring to mind? Write your thoughts in the space provided. The following incomplete sentences are meant to be a catalyst for your reflection.*

The mission of peace today means . . .

Harmony and forgiveness can come to fruition if I . . .

I understand the challenge of peace in the world to mean . . .

Human dignity is enhanced when I . . .

The work of justice challenges me to . . .

The human community will be served better if I . . .

Earth and its inhabitants will be united if I . . .

Memorable People:

Saint Irene (d. 304) is considered the patron Saint for peace. This Saint and her sisters (Saints Agape and Chionia, who were burned alive) were arrested during the Diocletian persecutions for possessing Christian scriptures. Irene was forced to work in a house of prostitution, but when no one would touch her, her captors then either burned her or she was shot with an arrow.

Did You Know?

Prior to receiving Holy Communion, Catholics offer one another a sign of Christ's peace. This liturgical gesture today is usually a handshake or an embrace, but originally it was a kiss. Sharing "the kiss of peace" has had various meanings throughout Christian history, including communion, reconciliation, and affirmation of prayer.

The Church Says:

While addressing the world situation, the Church's teaching on the challenge of peace rests on Scripture, where many treatments of peace may be found. One thread, however, is clear in the Old Testament concept of covenant. Peace is not merely negative, that is, the absence of conflict. Rather, it is the perfection of the covenant relationship between God and God's people that brings about the well-being of individuals and the whole community of faith. The Hebrew word shalom refers to a total harmony with nature, God, and self that issues forth in justice and is experienced in a fruitful land and people, whose needs are provided for and who dwell secure, free from fear and harm. The New Testament picks up this thread. Jesus ushers in the messianic kingdom and is the very presence of God among us. God brings to fulfillment what we cannot achieve on our own—the peace of a people covenanted to their Creator. This peace is the gift of the Risen Christ to the Church.

In light of the situation of the modern world and informed by this biblical teaching, contemporary Popes and the Second Vatican Council have spoken about peace. Pope John XXIII in *Pacem in Terris* ("Peace on Earth," 1963) addressed himself to all persons of good will, not just those within the Church, and urged a concerted effort by the nations to reduce the threat of mass destruction. The council not only taught that all war should be outlawed by international agreement but pointed out that the arms race and nuclear deterrence does not eliminate war but only aggravates the situation. Furthermore, the council emphasized that the foundation for world peace is built upon eliminating the causes of discord by providing for the legitimate needs of all people. Pope Paul VI issued an encyclical letter in 1967 entitled Populorum progressio ("Progress of Peoples") that further developed the council's teaching. He passionately decried the exploitation of the Third World and appealed to the consciences of First and Second World countries, declaring, "Development is the new name for peace."

For This Week:

I want to remember:

I want to put my faith into action by:

Questions to Explore

Prayer for the Week

Lord, make me an instrument of your peace;
where there is hatred, let me sow love;
where there is injury, pardon;
where there is doubt, faith;
where there is despair, hope;
where there is darkness, light;
where there is sadness, joy.

O divine Master, grant that I may not so much seek
to be consoled as to console,
to be understood as to understand,
to be loved as to love.
For it is in giving that we receive,
it is in pardoning that we are pardoned,
it is in dying that we are born to eternal life.
Amen.
        (Prayer of Saint Francis of Assisi)

Third Sunday of Easter

Scripture:

Acts 3:13–15, 17–19
Psalm 4:2, 4, 7–8, 9
1 John 2:1–5
Luke 24:35–48

Focus:

EVANGELIZATION
(BEARING WITNESS)

Reflection

Directions: *Recall your journey of faith from your earliest memories to the present. Consider these questions, then write your responses:*

Who has influenced you in your faith and in what way?

Who has been an example to you of what it means to be a follower of Jesus Christ?

What is the "Good News"?

Quotable Quotes:

Quotes from *Evangelii Nuntiandi* (*"Evangelization in the Modern World,"* Pope Paul VI, 1975):
"The Church exists in order to evangelize."

It is unthinkable that a person should accept the Word and give himself to the Kingdom without becoming a person who bears witness to it and proclaims it in his turn.

Above all, the Gospel must be proclaimed by witness.

Did You Know?

The word "gospel" means good news. Each of the Gospel writers has been assigned a distinctive symbol:
- Matthew: a man because his account begins with the human ancestry of Christ
- Mark: a lion, a desert animal, because his account begins with John the Baptist who cries out in the wilderness
- Luke: an ox, an animal used for sacrifice, because his account begins with Zechariah entering the Holy of Holies to offer sacrifice
- John: an eagle, a bird that can fly highest in the sky, because his account begins with words that take the reader soaring into the heavens

The Church Says:

"Evangelization" is derived from the Greek and means to announce good news, good tidings. The Good News of Salvation has a specific content, a message that we can talk about, teach, and explain. This content refers to a person whose words and deeds saved us, Jesus Christ. The Son of God, our Lord and Savior, continues to be the One who saves us, because he is, as the Gospel states (John 14:6), "the way, and the truth, and the life."

Through the Holy Spirit, Christ is experienced in the Church, his Body. Sharing our faith and lifestyle and celebrating Sacraments with other members of the Church, we are gifted with his presence.

Evangelization is a multifaceted endeavor. We assist others to embrace the message of Good News; we do this first of all by embracing the person, Jesus Christ, and his Body, the Church. Surrendering to that loving embrace, disciples of the Lord witness by word and deed to the Salvation won for us in Christ. We Catholics, therefore, believe that the multifaceted enterprise of evangelization cannot occur without conversion within the evangelizer. The dynamic of evangelization profoundly changes us as we put on the new person of Christ in our lives.

For This Week:

I want to remember:

I want to put my faith into action by:

Questions to Explore

Prayer for the Week

God of heaven, God of truth, a people once in darkness has listened to your Word and followed your Son as he rose from the tomb.

Hear the prayer of this newborn people and strengthen your Church to answer your call to mission.

May we rise and come forth into the light of day to stand in your presence until eternity dawns.

We ask this through Christ our Lord. Amen.

(Adapted from Evening Prayer of the Liturgy of the Hours for the Third Sunday of Easter)

Fourth Sunday of Easter

Scripture:

Acts 4:8–12
Psalm 118:1, 8–9, 21–23, 26, 28, 29
1 John 3:1–2
John 10:11–18

Focus:

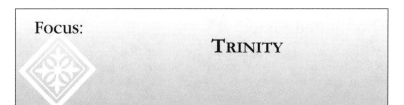

TRINITY

Reflection

1. *Jesus tells us his relationship with us is like that of his own relationship with the Father. Jesus also gives a specific image of being our good shepherd. We know Jesus' voice, and Jesus knows our voice. A few characteristics of Jesus' relationship with his Father and of his relationship with us are given below. Add to this list from your understanding.*

JESUS' RELATIONSHIP WITH GOD
- *Intimate*
- *Total*
- *Union*
- *One Spirit*
- *Tender*
- *Caring*

JESUS' RELATIONSHIP WITH US
- *Intimate*
- *Complete*
- *Oneness*
- *Present*

2. *God, though One, is revealed as Three Persons: Father, Son, and Holy Spirit. These Three Persons are in a relationship of love. Write below your response to this: What do you think it means for us that God, in God's very being and nature, is in loving relationship?*

Quotable Quote:

" This prayer of Blessed Elizabeth of the Trinity expresses communion with the Trinity:
O my God, Trinity whom I adore, help me forget myself . . . to establish myself in you . . . as if my soul were already in eternity. May nothing . . . make me leave you. . . . may each minute bring me more deeply into your mystery! Grant my soul peace. Make it your heaven, your beloved dwelling. . . . May I be there, whole and entire . . . adoring . . . given over to your creative action. "

Did You Know?

When the Church gathers in prayer, she prays in the name of the Trinity. Liturgical prayer is usually addressed to God, prayed through Christ, in union with the Holy Spirit. The Sign of the Cross, with words and gestures, is frequently used at the beginning of prayer. A doxology, a prayer of praise to the Trinity, is often used to end prayer.

The Church Says:

The One God has been revealed by God as a trinity of persons. Each Person of God is distinct, yet all Persons of God are one. In revealing this to us, God has not only given us information about who God is, but has shared with us God's very nature. The Three Persons of God—Father, Son, and Holy Spirit—are one in an intimate and loving relationship. They are all equal and truly God. When one Person of God is present, so are all three. Christ in his human life helps us understand who God is. The Holy Spirit continues to make available to us the presence of Christ. The Nicene Creed, professed every Sunday at Mass, states clearly that the persons of God are one in being.

God reveals to us that God is a God of love. God has adopted us as children in Christ through the Holy Spirit. God's action unfolds in the work of creation, in the whole history of Salvation, and in the ongoing mission of Christ. Through the Spirit, Christ's mission is continued in the mission of the Church.

As Catholics, we are called to faith in a loving, triune God. This loving, relational God invites us to live this same relationship of love within the Christian community, and indeed, within the entire human family. Christians thus see the presence and action of the Blessed Trinity in all dimensions of life. Whether alone or with the gathered community, we pray in the name of God, through Christ, and in union with the Holy Spirit.

For This Week:

I want to remember:

I want to put my faith into action by:

Questions to Explore

Prayer for the Week

Loving and gracious God,
may we come to know you more fully
as a loving parent ever at our side,
watching over us and providing for all we need.
May we live and move
and have our being in Christ,
in all that Christ has shown us.
May we follow the shepherd's
voice more closely.
Open us to the action
and power of the Spirit
so alive and present in our lives and world.
Glory be to the Father, and to the Son,
and to the Holy Spirit.
As it was in the beginning,
is now, and will be forever.
Amen.

Fifth Sunday of Easter

Scripture:

Acts 9:26–31
Psalm 22:26–27, 28, 30, 31–32
1 John 3:18–24
John 15:1–8

Focus:

THE CHURCH AS THE BODY OF CHRIST

Reflection

Directions: *The images found in the metaphor of the vine and branches are many. Spend some time reflecting upon their meaning as it relates to your life in the exercise provided. Listed below are the key images. Think about the implications of the image presented and then write down the meaning for your journey of faith in community.*

Jesus the vine—Life-giving nutrients flow through the vine
God the vinegrower—care and wisdom are needed to produce abundant fruit
We the branches—fruit grows and ripens on the branches
Pruning the barren branches
Fruit cannot grow apart from the branches
Withered, pruned branches are thrown into the fire
God is glorified when you bear abundant fruit

Questions

1. *What parallels do you find between the Church and the image in today's Gospel?*

2. *How have you experienced the abundant fruit of this parish community—this initiation community?*

Quotable Quote:

"Little children, let us love, not in word or speech, but in truth and action."
(1 John 3:18)

Did You Know?

Saint Joan of Arc (d. 1431) responded at her trial to a question put to her by the judges. She summed up the faith and the good sense of believers who are members of the Body of Christ when she said, "About Jesus Christ and the Church, I simply know they're just one thing, and we shouldn't complicate the matter"(Acts of the Trial of Joan of Arc).

The Church Says:

The Greek word ekklesia, meaning "church," is a reference to the People of God. Literally it means "gathering" or "assembly." For us today, "church" means the gathering of a people who were formerly divided and scattered 0by the chaos of sin, and now are brought together through Christ's Death and Resurrection.

This gathering is not, however, a place, but an organic body. As a growing, living organism, the Body of Christ —the Church—is both a visible society and a spiritual community. Human and divine, the Church forms a mystical body that transcends worldly dimensions. This means that one with Christ, the Church created in Jesus Christ exists in order that God's freeing love might be communicated to everyone.

Through the empowerment of the charisms, or Gifts, of the Holy Spirit the Church lives out her mission, to be a sacrament, or sign, of the union of all humanity with God for the Salvation of all through Jesus' work of Redemption. The Church is the visible sign of God's love extended for all through communion with Christ, under the presence and power of the Holy Spirit.

For This Week:

I want to remember:

I want to put my faith into action by:

Questions to Explore

Prayer for the Week

Christ our vine,
let the overflowing waters of your love
flow through us
that we might bear fruit in loving our brothers
and sisters.
God the vinegrower,
prune and remove
all sin, doubt, and clutter from our lives.
Spirit of love,
hover over the chaos of our lives
that we might find truth, peace, and serenity.
We pray that you, God the Father, Son,
and Holy Spirit, be glorified in the Body of Christ,
the Church.
Bless us, your people,
that all will know you
by our love for one another.
Amen.

Sixth Sunday of Easter

Scripture:

Acts 10:25–26, 34–35, 44–48
Psalm 98:1, 2–3, 3–4
1 John 4:7–10 [or: 1 John 4:11–16
when the Ascension is celebrated
next Sunday]
John 15:9–17 [or: John 17:11–19
(when the Ascension is celebrated next Sunday)]

Focus:

LOVE, THE SOUL OF
AN APOSTOLATE

Reflection

Directions: *Make a list of the many ways you have witnessed, observed, experienced, heard, or read about love in the past days or weeks. Then share some or all of your list with one other person. Finally, answer the following:*

What do you understand by the words about love in today's readings?

Memorable People:

Saint John Paul II promulgated an apostolic exhortation in 1988 devoted solely to examining the vocation of lay members of Christ's faithful people *(Christifideles laici)*. He describes how lay efforts in the apostolate are nourished at the Eucharistic table and lead to individual and group activities showing love of neighbor He maintains that the proliferation of governmental and private assistance agencies will never remove the need for believers to help their neighbor in charity

Did You Know?

The Christian Family Movement (CFI), the Catholic Worker, and the Association of Catholic Trade Unionists are three early examples of the initiative of the laity in addressing social reform. But the organizations formed by lay Catholics are not restricted to the family or labor issues; they also address social concerns such as racism (Catholic Interracial Council), the arts (National Academy of Arts), history (American Catholic Historical Society), and peacemaking (Pax Christi, St. Ansgar's Society).

The Church Says:

Since the baptized are the Church, they are called to respond to the call of God to put their lives at the service of the Reign of God and to labor to build up the kingdom of Christ throughout the world. The apostolate of pastors in communities of the faithful cannot be truly effective without the assistance of lay Christians who themselves proclaim to all men and women the message of salvation entrusted to us.

The mission of Christians in the world may take many forms, exhibiting a wide variety of activity. Love is the soul of this diverse apostolate and Christians draw their motivation for it and the strength to carry it out from the Eucharist, which is the "source and summit of the Christian life" (SC 47). In their participation in the mission of Jesus to the world they witness to the love God has shown us in Jesus, and by their deliberate efforts place their own love at the service of Jesus' mission in his Church.

For This Week:

I want to remember:

I want to put my faith into action by:

Questions to Explore

Prayer for the Week

"We beseech you, O Lord, to grant us your help and protection.
Deliver the afflicted, pity the lowly, raise the fallen, reveal yourself to the needs, heal the sick, and bring home your wandering people. Feed the hungry, ransom the captive, support the weak, comfort the faint-hearted.
Let all the nations of the earth know that you alone are God, that Jesus Christ is your child, and that we are your people and the sheep of your pasture."

(Prayers of the Saints, Woodeen Koenig-Bricker, San Francisco: HarperSanFrancisco, 1996, p.111)

Seventh Sunday of Easter

Scripture:

Acts 1:15–17, 20–26
Psalm 103:1–2, 11–12, 19–20
1 John 4:11–16
John 17:11–19

Focus:

HIERARCHICAL NATURE OF teh CHURCH

Reflection

1. *The early Church, under the leadership of Peter, prayed to the Holy Spirit, then chose Matthias as an Apostle to replace Judas. Through Baptism into Christ we are called to be apostles, to witness to and share in the mission of Christ to bring about God's reign. In the space provided, list some qualities that you believe are important for apostles to possess.*

   Important Qualities for Apostles:

2. *Listed below are categories of people who have received the Sacrament of Holy Orders, and thus have a particular role in the Church's hierarchy of leadership. Put as many names as you know that belong under each heading. Then write the particular functions that belong to this office. When you are finished, you might want to share what you have written with a Catholic.*

	POPE	BISHOP	PRIEST	DEACON
Names				
Function				

Memorable People:

Saint Catherine of Siena (1347–80), Doctor of the Church, persuaded Pope Gregory XI to return the papacy to Rome from Avignon, France. God spoke to the Church through her mystical experiences: "I am not a respecter of persons or status but of holy desires. In whatever situation people may be, let their will be good and holy, and they will be pleasing to me." (*In Her Words*, Amy Oden, ed., Abingdon Press, Nashville, 1994, p. 199).

Did You Know?

In order to express collegiality among bishops, from the time of the early Church it has been the tradition for at least three bishops to participate in the ordination of a new bishop.

The Church Says:

All members of the Church are one through their Baptism in Christ. Dating back to the beginning of the Church, particular people have taken on roles of leadership. In the Acts of the Apostles, Peter is often seen as holding the leadership role among the Apostles. Church leadership from the time of Peter to the present day has been passed on in the Church in what is called "apostolic succession."

The entire Church communicates Christ's truth and grace. Yet the Church requires some authority to preserve its identity, unity, and to make decisions and resolve conflicts. Church leadership is service-oriented, since all in the Church follow Christ who came to serve. Leadership in the Church is not separate from the rest of the Christian community. Church governance is exercised in communion with the entire Church.

Church leadership exists in a hierarchy, or ordering, of roles. All the baptized share in the priesthood of Christ and all in the Church are equal. Some members of the Church by the grace of the Holy Spirit are called to leadership in the Church and receive the Sacrament of Holy Orders. The hierarchy of roles in the Church includes the Pope, who is the bishop of Rome, bishops, priests, deacons, and laity. Religious brothers and sisters are part of the Church's laity and do not receive Holy Orders. Each of the orders in the Church has particular functions, including the laity, who have their particular apostolic role.

Throughout the history of the Church to the present age the Holy Spirit has continued to call individuals to leadership in the Church. Thus, the Spirit is involved in the ongoing structural life of the Church.

For This Week:

I want to remember:

I want to put my faith into action by:

Questions to Explore

Prayer for the Week

*Loving God, we thank you for the gift
of those who give their lives
to lead your Church.
Bless our Church leaders
with sincere and humble hearts.
Make us all true servants
of your Word and your love.
Give us the grace to live in the world
and not belong to the world.
In all things may we keep our hearts
set on Christ,
who is our guide and Redeemer.
Count us among your apostles.
We pray in Jesus' name.
Amen.*

Pentecost Sunday

Scripture:

Acts 2:1–11
Psalm 104:1, 24, 29–30, 31, 34
1 Corinthians 12:3–7, 12–13
  [or: Galatians 5:16–25]
John 20:19–23 [or: John 15:26–27;
  16:12–15]

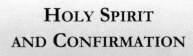

Focus:

HOLY SPIRIT
AND CONFIRMATION

Reflection

Directions: *In the space provided jot down your feelings and insights as you listened once again to the proclamation of the Gospel of John.*

Questions

1. *When have you experienced your fears being transformed into peace and joy, as did the Apostles through the power of the Holy Spirit?*

2. *What does Jesus' action of "breathing the Spirit" upon the first followers mean to you today?*

3. *What evidence of the connection between forgiveness and the power of the Holy Spirit have you seen among the followers of Jesus today?*

Did You Know?

The seven Gifts of the Holy Spirit, expressed in the Church's prayer at Confirmation, are: wisdom, understanding, judgment, courage, knowledge, reverence, and wonder and awe.

The Church Says:

The Solemnity of Pentecost Sunday celebrates the outpouring of the Spirit on the disciples. It is the birthday of the Church.

The Holy Spirit continues the presence of Christ in the Church and the world today. The names given to the Spirit indicate the characteristics of this Spirit—Spirit of God, Breath of God, Paraclete (Greek word meaning "called to the side of"), and Advocate. The Holy Spirit enkindles our faith. Thus, the Church teaches that it is impossible to know God, the Father, or Jesus, the Son, without the inspiration of the Holy Spirit. The Holy Spirit proceeds or flows from the love between the Father and the Son. This Church teaching, known as the Trinity, indicates that we believe and proclaim in the Nicene Creed, that the Holy Spirit shares in the same divine nature as the Father and the Son.

In the Sacrament of Confirmation we celebrate the full pouring forth of the Holy Spirit upon the follower of Christ. Linked with Baptism and Eucharist, Confirmation is one of the Sacraments of Initiation by which the faithful are more perfectly bound to the Church and are enriched with the special strength to become true witnesses of Christ. Confirmation, usually conferred by a bishop, includes the laying on of hands and the anointing with Sacred Chrism (scented oil consecrated on Holy Thursday). The laying on of hands symbolizes the descent of the Holy Spirit and the anointing symbolizes healing and investing with power (as in the anointing of kings and prophets in the Old Testament). The Holy Spirit, giver of divine gifts, empowers us to live as Christians—active members of the Church, boldly witnessing the Good News of Jesus in the world today.

For This Week:

I want to remember:

I want to put my faith into action by:

Questions to Explore

Prayer for the Week

To celebrate Pentecost this week,
pray this at mealtime with your family members.

Verse: Come, Holy Spirit, fill the hearts of your faithful.
Response: And kindle in them the fire of your love.
Verse: Send forth your Spirit and they shall be created.
Response: And you will renew the face of the earth.

Let us pray.

Lord,
by the light of the Holy Spirit
you have taught the hearts of your faithful.
In the same Spirit
help us to relish what is right
and always rejoice in your consolation.
We ask this through Christ our Lord.
Amen.

ORDINARY
TIME

Second Sunday in Ordinary Time

Scripture:

1 Samuel 3:3b–10, 19
Psalm 40:2, 4, 7–8, 8–9, 10
1 Corinthians 6:13c–15a, 17–20
John 1:35–42

Focus:

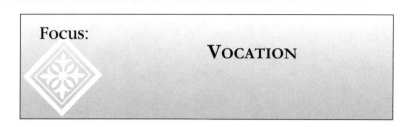

VOCATION

Reflection

Directions: *Take some time to reflect on people and events that have led you to this time and place on your journey of faith.*

Who has helped you to know Christ and in what ways have they helped you?

What events have helped you to know Christ and in what way have these events led you?

How have you experienced Christ's invitation or his question, "What are you looking for"?

How have you responded?

Quotable Quotes:

Pope Saint John Paul II wrote, *"The Gospel image of the vine and the branches reveals to us . . . the call to growth and a continual process of maturation, of always bearing much fruit. . . ."*

"People are approached in liberty by God who calls everyone to grow, develop and bear fruit. A person cannot put off a response nor cast off personal responsibility in the matter."
(CL 57.1 & 57.4)

The Church Says:

All human beings are created by God for the purpose of knowing and loving the Creator. We believe that we are called by God ultimately to share in the divine life. In Jesus, the fullness of this Revelation is made manifest. The vocation to be a disciple is the basis for the believer's joy in life and is the foundation of our Salvation. Baptism is the Sacrament that celebrates this calling in Christ and incorporates us into the life of the Risen Lord. The invitation to become a disciple and a member of the kingdom is extended to every person on the face of the Earth. Through the grace of God, disciples make more disciples.

In our Catholic understanding there are three aspects of vocation:

Christ sent forth the Apostles, who in turn handed on the Gospel to succeeding generations. Impelled by the love of Christ, believers act on their vocation and therefore continue to spread the Good News of Salvation throughout the world by professing the faith, living it as a loving brother or sister, and celebrating it in prayer and in liturgy.

Another aspect of vocation is experienced in the structured way each believer lives out his or her baptismal commitment. These ways include: married life, single life, the priesthood, and the consecrated life as a member of a religious community.

All believers are called to be holy as Christ taught us. This holiness of life is made possible with the assistance of the Church. All the activities of the Church are to minister to people so that their sanctification might render glory to God.

For This Week:

I want to remember:

I want to put my faith into action by:

Questions to Explore	Prayer for the Week
	Each day this week, recall a person or event that has helped you on your journey of faith. Spend time reflecting on the way(s) in which the person or event has touched your life.
	Then give thanks to God for the person or event.

Third Sunday in Ordinary Time

Scripture:

Jonah 3:1–5, 10
Psalm 25:4–5, 6–7, 8–9
1 Corinthians 7:29–31
Mark 1:14–20

Focus:

SIN AND REPENTANCE

Reflection

Directions: *When Jesus called Simon and Andrew, James and John to follow him, they immediately abandoned their nets and followed him.*

What attracts you to following Jesus?

What concerns do you have about following him?

What do you need to leave behind to follow Jesus completely?

Quotable Quote:

> *When the assembly prays the Confiteor, "I confess," at Mass, they ask for the community's prayerful support.*
> *They pray: "I confess to almighty God and to you, my brothers and sisters, that I have greatly sinned,*
> *in my thoughts and in my words, in what I have done and in what I have failed to do, . . .*
> *therefore I ask . . . you, my brothers and sisters, to pray for me to the Lord our God."*
> (Penitential Act, *Roman Missal*)

Did You Know?

Catholics refer to the Sacrament of Penance and Reconciliation as "going to confession." What we confess first and foremost is the gracious love and generous mercy of God who draws us back to a close relationship.

Saint John Paul II asked forgiveness on behalf of the Church's past faults and failings. He invited all believers to repentance so that the Church could enter the third millennium of Christianity renewed.

The Church Says:

God created everything in love, and an initial harmony existed. God's creation was wounded and scarred by sin, which is described in the Genesis account of Adam and Eve. Sin destroyed the initial harmony of creation, led to friction in human relationships, and brought decay and death into the world.

Sin is a failure to love God, neighbor, and self. It offends reason, truth, and right conscience. It is a personal act or omission that in essence is a turning away from God.

Personal sin is described as mortal and venial. Sin is mortal, or "deadly," when it is so grave that it destroys charity in one's entire being. Mortal sin requires full knowledge of the deed or omission and total consent to this evil. Venial sin wounds but does not destroy charity. It impedes growth in virtue and moral goodness and is to be avoided.

The Church acknowledges the presence of social sin, which exists when communal structures are evil and contribute to and influence individual sin. Yet sin is always a personal act or omission.

In light of the reality of the presence of sin and the struggle against it, God continues to call us back to full relationship out of love. God always initiates our turning back to the light of love. Out of love, God sent Christ to free us from the bondage of sin. Through the entire Church community we are given support for ongoing conversion and growth in holiness.

For This Week:

I want to remember:

I want to put my faith into action by:

Questions to Explore

Prayer for the Week

Loving God,
you sent Christ who calls us to follow him.
Attract us to Christ's love and goodness.
Let us always believe
in the magnitude of your love
which seeks us out and offers forgiveness.
May we never fear to bring you our whole selves,
with our hearts of love and our sinful failings.
Give us the desire
to acknowledge our wrongdoings.
Keep our eyes focused on the life you offer us.
We pray through Christ, our saving Lord.
Amen.

Fourth Sunday in Ordinary Time

Scripture:

Deuteronomy 18:15–20
Psalm 95:1–2, 6–7, 7–9
1 Corinthians 7:32–35
Mark 1:21–28

Focus:

JESUS AS PROPHET, TEACHER, AND LORD

Reflection

Directions: *Having listened once again to the proclamation of Mark's Gospel, describe Jesus' power to amaze and capture your heart. Use the roles of Jesus—teacher, prophet and Lord—and the sentences from the Gospel to guide your writing.*

JESUS THE TEACHER
"He taught them as one having authority." (Mark 1:22)

JESUS THE PROPHET
"He commands even the unclean spirits, and they obey him." (Mark 1:27)

JESUS IS LORD
"They were all amazed." (Mark 1:27)

Questions

1. *What simple changes have taken place in your life as you have come to know Jesus, our teacher, prophet, and Lord?*

2. *What challenges have you experienced as you struggle to hear and obey the teaching authority of Jesus, Lord of your life?*

3. *How can you grow in your understanding of Jesus?*

4. *What commitment will you make at this time?*

Did You Know?

Jesus as prophet, teacher, and Lord is portrayed in a sixth-century mosaic found in the Archiepiscopal Chapel at Ravenna, Italy, that can be described as "Christ militant." In the mosaic, Jesus stands before the mountains (from which prophets speak). He is dressed as a soldier, balancing his Cross like a sword across his shoulders with his right hand. In his left hand he holds an open book containing his teaching upon whose pages is written *Ego sum via, veritas, et vita* ("I am the way, the truth, and the life"). Under his feet (for he is Lord of all) cower a defeated lion and a snake (Jaroslav Pelikan, *Jesus Through the Centuries. His Place in the History of Culture.* Yale University Press, New Haven, 1985, p. 7).

The Church Says:

Jesus unfolds the Reign of God in his very person, in his ministry, Death, and Resurrection. We are challenged to extend this reign—a kingdom of harmony, justice, and truth—by listening to Jesus' teachings, heeding his prophetic and paradoxical challenges, and offering all honor and praise to him, the Risen Lord of all creation.
A prophet like Moses, Jesus mediates between God and humanity. But his words and works have effects according to divine power. He fulfills and is the high point of the prophetic tradition begun in Moses. He is the new Moses, the new lawgiver, leader, teacher, prophet, and deliverer. We believe that Jesus is not merely the greatest prophet, but is the eternal Son of God who became one with humanity in all things but sin.

The authority of his teaching, which encompassed his entire life, his ministry, his words and actions, his redeeming Death and Resurrection, astonished those who witnessed his healing power and heard his words. For believers today, Jesus' teaching opens up the mystery of the kingdom to all who will listen and act.

His title, Kyrios (Greek) or Lord, indicates that the power, honor, and glory that are the Father's are also Jesus'. His name is above every other name, for in Jesus we are saved from sin, set free from death, and offered a place in the kingdom as heirs and children of God. As we place our trust totally in the spellbinding authority of Jesus, we are freed to live up to our full stature, transformed by God's love, and empowered to take our place in the kingdom through the power of the Holy Spirit.

For This Week:

I want to remember:

I want to put my faith into action by:

Questions to Explore

  ## Prayer for the Week

God, Creator of this vast universe,
we give you thanks.
You have given us the prophet Moses
as a sign of your continual presence and guidance.
You placed your Word on his lips and
in the mouths of the prophets
throughout the history of the Israelites.
You sent us your Son, Jesus,
the Word made flesh, to announce a new era,
the eruption of your kingdom of harmony
and deliverance.
As we journey in faith,
open our hearts and minds to hear your Word
and heed its message.
We pray in the power of your Spirit, for ever and ever.
Amen.

Fifth Sunday in Ordinary Time

Scripture:

Job 7:1–4, 6–7
Psalm 147:1–2, 3–4, 5–6
1 Corinthians 9:16–19, 22–23
Mark 1:29–39

Focus:

THE PROBLEM OF EVIL

Reflection

Directions: *Spend some time each day listening to the news or reading the newspaper or a news magazine, looking for headlines and articles depicting physical and moral evils, as well as articles about blessings and joys. Ponder the ways in which the Paschal Mystery is present in our world. Record your thoughts and feelings.*

Quotable Quote:

. . . in order to perceive the true answer to the 'why' of suffering, we must look to the revelation of divine love, the ultimate source of the meaning of everything that exists. Love is also the richest source of the meaning of suffering, which always remains a mystery: we are conscious of the insufficiency and inadequacy of our explanation. Christ causes us to enter into the mystery and to discover the 'why' of suffering, as far as we are capable of grasping the sublimity of divine love. (Pope John Paul II, SD 13)

Did You Know?

The cross attributed to Saint Francis (d. 1226) is a flat panel upon which is painted a figure of the dying Christ, whose twisted body is helped up by angels and surrounded by figures representing his mother, the disciple John, and others. Above the head of Jesus, on the top vertical end of the cross, is depicted the Saints above whom can be seen the hand of God the Father outstretched in blessing over the Son. It is a vivid reminder of our Catholic belief in the redemptive aspect of Christ's suffering and Death. (This cross is also called the San Damiano Cross.)

The Church Says:

Through the eyes of faith Catholics perceive the reasons for evil in the world. We acknowledge two distinct kinds of evil: moral and physical. Moral evil is evidenced in Original Sin and personal sin. Physical evil is evidenced in phenomena such as natural disasters, pain, and physical debilitation due to sickness, physical and mental disabilities, and accidents.

Through Divine Revelation in Scripture we understand that Adam received original holiness and justice not simply for himself but for all humanity. In a similar fashion, by yielding to temptation and turning away from God, his choice has affected human nature. Thus, we are born into a fallen state called "Original Sin," a reality we contract because we are human, not because we commit it. Unlike Original Sin, personal sin is something we commit, something for which we are responsible.

The disruption and chaos experienced by physical evil is a consequence of Original Sin and is symbolized in Scripture by the loss of Eden. In spite of our experiences of this type of evil, we affirm that God is all-good and all-powerful. Any other affirmation would reduce what God is. The only way we can begin to grasp the problem of the existence of physical evil is by entering into the mystery of the great love that God has for us. Whatever happens in life, we know that God's love is constant. God's Son shared our suffering and death so that we might be redeemed and offered new life. He has also come to save us ultimately from all physical evil. Through the Church and in the power of the Spirit, Jesus continues to act as physician of our bodies and souls, extending to us God's healing love.

For This Week:

I want to remember:

I want to put my faith into action by:

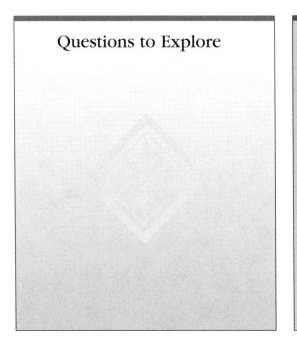

Questions to Explore

Prayer for the Week

Take time each evening to reflect on the activities of the day. Then pray the following:

For all the blessings of this day (name them), I give you thanks, O God.

For my words and actions that were sinful (name them), I ask your forgiveness, O God.

For the words and actions of others that caused me pain (name them), I offer forgiveness and ask for healing, O God.

Sixth Sunday in Ordinary Time

Scripture:

Leviticus 13:1–2, 44–46
Psalm 32:1–2, 5, 11
1 Corinthians 10:31–11:1
Mark 1:40–45

Focus:

SACRAMENT OF THE ANOINTING OF THE SICK

Reflection

Directions: *Recall the story of the leper Jesus cured. He was an outcast in society, and had to remain separated from the community. Then answer the following questions:*

1. *What do you think enabled the leper to come before Jesus and ask for healing?*

2. *What were the leper's thoughts, feelings, and beliefs?*

3. *What was the leper's perception of Jesus?*

Memorable People:

Saint Damien de Veuster, known as Father Damien (1840–1889), a missionary priest from Belgium, worked with lepers on the island of Molokai, Hawaii, in 1873. For sixteen years he served as pastor, counselor, physician, and undertaker. In 1884 he contracted leprosy, and died in March 1889.

Saint Dymphna, the patron Saint of the mentally ill whose feast day is May 15, in the seventh century escaped her father's torture by fleeing to Gheel, Belgium. Her relics were discovered there seven centuries later. A hospital for the mentally ill stands at the site.

Did You Know?

Viaticum is the final Holy Communion given to the sick who are near death. The word means "food for the journey," and thus indicates our belief that life does not end in death. Rather, those who die "in Christ" begin a new form of life, victorious in the Lord Jesus. At death, life is changed, not taken away.

The Church Says:

Serious sickness presents a critical time in a person's faith life, since it can lead to anguish, selfishness, and despair, or to a deeper faith and sense of what is truly essential in life. Anointing of the Sick proclaims God's kingdom and Christ's victory over sin and death through the Paschal Mystery.

The seriously ill person receives spiritual healing and physical healing as well, if it is God's desire, in addition to the Spirit's gift of strength. He or she is united to the Passion of Christ, and through this Sacrament human suffering is transformed. He or she becomes a sacrament to the Church of the true life God calls us to and of the value of human life.

Since Sacraments are part of the Church's liturgy and pastoral care, the presence of all or part of the parish community is desirable. The anointing may take place in a church at Sunday Mass, in a hospital, a nursing facility, or in a private home. A bishop or priest administers the Sacrament, after a Scripture reading, while praying these words: "Through this holy anointing may the Lord in his love and mercy help you with the grace of the Holy Spirit. May the Lord who frees you from sin save you and raise you up" (PCS5, 25). The person is anointed with the Oil of the Sick on the forehead and palms of the hands, or another part of the body, as suitable.

In the case of a person dying, this Sacrament, along with the reception of a final Eucharist, known as Viaticum ("food for the journey"), prepares the person for the journey to new life "in Christ."

For This Week:

I want to remember:

I want to put my faith into action by:

Questions to Explore

Prayer for the Week

Lord Jesus, we come before you
with our illnesses, our sins,
and with our faith.
Bring healing wherever it is needed.
Open our hearts to your touch.
Give us the generosity of spirit
to care for the sick,
to pray for their well-being,
and to touch them with our presence.
Make us instruments of your healing.
May we come to believe more firmly
in your power over sickness and death,
for you are Lord, now and for ever.
Amen.

Seventh Sunday in Ordinary Time

Scripture:

Isaiah 43:18–19, 21–22, 24b–25
Psalm 41:2–3, 4–5, 13–14
2 Corinthians 1: 18–22
Mark 2:1–12

Focus:

SACRAMENT OF PENANCE AND RECONCILIATION

Reflection

Directions: *As you place yourself into the story of the paralyzed man, write down your reactions and feelings as one of the companions who carried him to Jesus. Describe the faith it took to trust in Jesus' power to heal physical ailments. Express your astonishment at discovering Jesus' power to heal the soul through the forgiveness of sin. Re-enter the story, taking on the person of the paralyzed man and write down your insights.*

As friend of the paralyzed man:

As the paralyzed man:

Quotable Quotes:

Catholics believe that there is no experience of pain or sickness outside the reach of God's healing presence, and no sin so terrible that God cannot forgive it. In this vein, Saint Teresa of Jesus (Teresa of Ávila) (d. 1582) wrote the following prayer on her bookmark, "Let nothing disturb you, nothing frighten you; all things are passing; patient endurance attains all things; one whom God possesses wants nothing, for God alone suffices."
(PrySts 16)

The Church Says:

God's love for humankind is complete and unconditional. From this love flows God's mercy, which is unconditional and unending. God's mercy is an expression of God's desire to be reconciled with us, that is, to forgive our sins, heal our weaknesses, and set us free. In the Sacrament of Penance and Reconciliation we celebrate this merciful, forgiving God. Baptism is the font of new life and forgiveness, but for those who fall into sin after Baptism, this Sacrament is the sign and celebration of God's mercy.

The Holy Spirit moves us to recognize our sinfulness and instills in us a desire to be radically transformed. Prompted by God's grace, we experience true sorrow for our patterns of sinful actions and omissions. In the Sacrament we first express and celebrate the love of God, prompting us to seek a change of heart, proclaim our sorrow, and resolve to avoid sin. Second, we privately name, or confess, our sins to God through the priest who presides over this sacramental celebration. Because of the "sacramental seal," the priest can never reveal what we have confessed. Third, we are asked to make reparation for our sinful acts by performing a penance. This can be prayer, charitable works, service, and self-sacrifice. Finally, the priest, in the name of the Church, extends his hands over the head of the believer in blessing and prays in the name of the community of believers. the absolution, or words of forgiveness. This prayer expresses God's forgiveness and the reconciliation of the sinner to God's self and the community of believers.

For This Week:

I want to remember:

I want to put my faith into action by:

Questions to Explore

Prayer for the Week

God of mercy and hope,
we believe in your ongoing creation,
your continual care for humanity
and the world in which we live.
Reconcile our sinful hearts.
Restore the harmony that once existed
in Eden's garden.
Do not grow weary of our weaknesses.
Prepare our hearts as we anticipate
your anointing and sealing in the Holy Spirit.
Establish us as your people once again
a people called to bring about
Eden's peace and harmony together with you.
Through Jesus, who forgave the paralytic,
heal us in spirit, mind, and body.
Thus we pray, So be it! Amen!

Eighth Sunday in Ordinary Time

Scripture:

Hosea 2:16b, 17b, 21–22
Psalm 103:1–2, 3–4, 8, 10, 12–13
2 Corinthians 3:1b–6
Mark 2:18–22

Focus:

GOD'S LOVE FOR US

Reflection

Directions: *Take some time to reflect on marriage as a covenant. Name some married couples you admire. Reflect on why you selected them. Describe elements or qualities that you consider essential to a covenant relationship such as marriage.*

Questions

1. *Make a list of contracts that you have signed or witnessed.*

2. *Mark those that are the most serious, such as marriage, partnership, oath, mortgage, insurance.*

3. *What constitutes the seriousness of such a contract?*

Quotable Quotes:

"
Fish cannot drown in the water,
Birds cannot sink in the air,
Gold cannot perish in the refiner's fire.
This has God given to all creatures
To foster and seek their own nature,
How then can I withstand mine?
I must to God —
My father through nature,
My brother through humanity,
My bridegroom through love
His am I forever!
German mystic Mechtild of Magdeburg (1210–1297)
"

The Church Says:

God's love is faithful. The love of God is unwavering; it motivates what God does for us. Because of love for us, God chooses to enter into a covenant with us and make us his own. We can also be sure that in Jesus Christ that Covenant love of God is fully manifested. God's abundant love for us is shown in Jesus, who suffers and dies for us and after his Resurrection sends the Holy Spirit to form the Church to continue his ministry of love. It is not surprising, then, that the metaphors or images in Sacred Scripture that describe this loving God are frequently drawn from marriage and family life.

Some images of God are:

The image of God as "father" is not that of a domineering power figure, but rather of one who is communicating life to his own. Jesus refers to God as his "Father" and taught his disciples to pray to God as their loving Father as well.

God as "mother" is the image the prophet Isaiah (49:15) uses, where he asks on behalf of God, "Can a woman forget her nursing child, or show no compassion for the child of her womb? Even these may forget, yet I will not forget you."

The image of God as "lover," one interpretation of the Song of Songs (a Hebrew erotic love poem), is as an allegory symbolizing the relationship between Israel and God.

The image of God as "friend," the shared trust and mutual delight that friends have in each other, aptly describes the love of God for us. Jesus calls us his friends because he has shared everything with us (John 15:15).

For This Week:

I want to remember:

I want to put my faith into action by:

Questions to Explore	Prayer for the Week
	Act of Charity, or Love *"My God, I love you with my whole heart and soul, and above all things, because you are infinitely good and perfect, and most worthy of all my love; and for your sake I love my neighbor as myself. Mercifully grant, O my God, that having loved you on earth, I may love and enjoy you for ever in heaven."* (Catholic Prayer Book, p. 138)

Ninth Sunday in Ordinary Time

Scripture:

Deuteronomy 5:12–15
Psalm 81:3–4, 5–6, 6–8, 10–11
2 Corinthians 4:6–11
Mark 2:23–3:6 or 2:23–28

Focus:

**KEEP HOLY
THE LORD'S DAY**

Reflection

Directions: *In the books of Genesis and Exodus the Sabbath is described as a day of rest, a day to celebrate God's saving action of bringing the Jewish people to the promised land. Brainstorm realistic activities or concrete ways you might be called to keep the Sabbath holy in your life.*

Possible ways of keeping the Sabbath Day holy include:

1.

2.

3.

4.

Quotable Quote:

Aidan Kavanagh, a Benedictine monk and liturgist, has stated, *"The Sunday liturgy is not the church assembled to address itself. . . . The liturgy . . . summons the assembly to enact itself publicly for the life of the world . . . What one witnesses in the liturgy is the world being done as the world's Creator and Redeemer will the world to be done."* (Aidan Kavanagh, Elements of Rite, Pueblo Publishing Company, New York, 1982, p. 45–46)

Did You Know?

Upon making Christianity the religion of the empire, Emperor Constantine decreed as part of the civil law (A.D. 321) that everyone in the Roman Empire refrain from work or legal matters on Sunday (EncyCath 1230).

The Church Says:

In the Book of Genesis the story of God creating the world in six "days" and resting on the seventh is the biblical foundation for the celebration of the Sabbath as a day of rest. In the Book of Exodus the further meaning of the Sabbath as a remembrance of God's saving action bringing the people to the promised land is given. The Commandment to keep the Sabbath day holy is found in both Exodus and Deuteronomy as part of the Ten Commandments given through Moses. The Jewish people kept the Sabbath on Saturday, the seventh day.

Early Christians began to celebrate the Sabbath on the first day of the week, the day of the Resurrection of Jesus. The Church celebrates the entire Paschal Mystery, or the life, Death, and Resurrection of Jesus, every Sunday at Mass.

The Sunday liturgy takes precedence over other feasts because of the prominence of the Sunday celebration as the day of the Resurrection.

The Sunday celebration not only looks to the past, but is also thought of as the eighth day, pointing to the Lord's Day in the fullness of time. This eighth day prepares us for the eternal eighth day of full union with God.

The precepts of the Church specify that the faithful are bound to participate in the Mass on Sunday and on other holy days, except for grave reason, for example, in the case of sickness or the care of the sick and infants. Participating at Mass at a Saturday evening vigil Mass also fulfills this obligation. In addition, Catholics on Sunday are to enjoy rest and leisure, cease work, pray and reflect, and treasure the familial, cultural, social, and religious aspects of life.

For This Week:

I want to remember:

I want to put my faith into action by:

Questions to Explore

Prayer for the Week

Holy, holy, holy are you, Lord, our God.
Holy, too, are we, your people.
God, you give us the Sabbath as a day of rest,
*   as a day to remember*
*   that we are your holy people,*
*   as a day to remember*
*   your saving action in our lives,*
*   as a day to bring your goodness and light*
*   to our families, and to those in need.*
May we take Sabbath time
*   to rest from work and busyness.*
May we always remember
*   that we are your earthen vessels*
*   holding a great treasure,*
Christ our light. Amen.

Tenth Sunday in Ordinary Time

Scripture:

Genesis 3:9–15
Psalm 130:1–2, 3–4, 5–6, 7–8
2 Corinthians 4:13–15
Mark 3:20–35

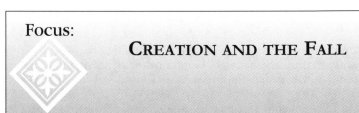

Focus:
CREATION AND THE FALL

Reflection

Directions: *Read and reread the poem. Use the space below to journal your insights, using these questions as a guide; In the light of the Creation story, God's gift of free will and Jesus command to do the will of God, what message do you find in the poem? What images seem to stand out for you?*

"A gracious Sabbath stood here while they stood"
Wendell Berry, *Sabbaths* (San Francisco: North Point Press, 1987), p. 83.

A gracious Sabbath stood here while they stood
Who gave our rest a haven.
Now fallen, they are given
To labor and distress.
These times we know much evil, little good
To steady us in faith
And comfort when our losses press
Hard on us, and we choose,
In panic or despair or both,
To keep what we will lose.

For we are fallen like the tress, our peace
Broken and so we must
Love where we cannot trust,
Trust where we cannot know.
And must await the wayward-coming grace
That joins living and dead,
Taking us where we would not go—
Into the boundless dark
When what was made has been unmade
The Maker comes to His work.

Questions

1. *What new insights do you now have regarding creation and the fall? Regarding the presence of evil and goodness in the world?*

2. *How can you use your free will to bring about more harmony and union among people? with Earth?*

Did You Know?

Based on the First Reading from Genesis, artists have traditionally depicted Mary as grinding the serpent under her heel. Numerous paintings, murals, and statues show the serpent groveling, attempting to bite her, but failing as the Mother of God raises her sandal and prepares to completely smash evil.

The Church Says:

The Church's teaching on creation and the fall are significant for our understanding of our Redemption in and through Christ. Yet the full power of these concepts are fully revealed through images. The wisdom of the Yahwist author in calling upon the images found in the prevailing creation myths of that time and culture yielded the Genesis story. The truth conveyed is that the breach of harmony between God and humanity was due to a sin of prideful disobedience.

God, the creator of all things, continues to create the universe and all that is in it. There is an order and an innate goodness in all of creation, particularly in humankind, fashioned in God's image and likeness.

The fall brought sin-disharmony-evil into the world, tainting the whole of human history. This fallen state, described as Original Sin, accounts for the disorder and strife we experience. The relationship of trust and communion humankind has with God is damaged. As were our first parents, we are free to choose this union with God or to reject and disobey it.

Yet we are not abandoned by God, for we have been sent a Savior to reestablish the intimacy and communion that was broken. Our hope is found in the self-sacrificing love of Jesus. In Christ the entire cosmos, including humanity, is made a new creation raised up into that intimate community with God.

For This Week:

I want to remember:

I want to put my faith into action by:

Questions to Explore

Prayer for the Week

God, you created humankind out of love, breathing into us your divine breath and making us in your image. Yet we failed to obey your commands, desiring to set ourselves as up as idols. Human pride and disobedience caused our fall, introducing sin, shame, mistrust, and evil into the harmonious world you created. Still you did not leave us to languish in our sin, choosing instead to send us your only Son to save and redeem us from that universal fall. And so we give you praise and rejoice in the One you sent, who healed the breach, restoring us to union with you. All honor and glory to God our Creator, Redeemer, and Sanctifier. Amen.

Eleventh Sunday in Ordinary Time

Scripture:

Ezekiel 17:22–24
Psalm 92:2–3, 13–14, 15–16
2 Corinthians 5:6–10
Mark 4:26–34

Focus:

THE CHURCH AND THE KINGDOM OF GOD

Reflection

Directions: Find a park, a nature preserve, an arboretum, or a place in your neighborhood that offers some plants, shrubs, and trees. Take some time to observe the vegetation and the animal world. Think about the wonders of creation. Notice the harmony and balance of nature. Ponder what nature has to teach us about God and God's relationship with all creation.

Questions

1. *With what group or organizations do you associate? List them under one of the first three categories.*

SOCIAL   PROFESSIONAL   POLITICAL   CHURCH

2. *Briefly describe the purpose of each organization you list. Then consider the fourth heading, Church. What words or phrases listed under the first three headings do you also associate with Church?*

Quotable Quotes:

"Pope Saint John Paul II wrote: *"The Church herself, then, is the vine in the Gospel. She is mystery because the very life and love of the Father, Son and Holy Spirit are the gift gratuitously offered to all those who are born of water and the Holy Spirit . . . and called to relive the very communion of God and to manifest it and communicate it in history [mission]. . . ." (CL 8.5)*"

The Church Says:

Christ came proclaiming the Kingdom of God, calling all to repentance from sin, announcing the Good News of Salvation and the new life he offered. With Christ's coming, the Kingdom of God was inaugurated. We believe that although the kingdom is present here and now, it is not yet fully realized. When Christ comes a second time, he will bring about the fullness of the Kingdom of God. The reality that sustains us, prepares us for, and moves us closer toward that Second Coming is the Church.

The Church is the Body of Christ, in whom all individual members are united. The Church is related to Christ as bride to bridegroom. It does not see itself as simply a collection of individuals but as members of the Church who have been called out of a former way of life, called away from sin, and have been joined together in the Spirit by Christ himself. Its goal is precisely life in Christ, that is, Salvation and the restoration of all things.

The Church exists because people need Salvation. The Second Vatican Council in Lumen Gentium (16) states that "the Church is necessary for salvation: the one Christ is mediator and the way of salvation; he is present to us in this body which is the Church. Christ himself explicitly asserted the necessity of faith and Baptism (cf. Mark 16:16; John 3:5), and thereby affirmed the necessity of the Church which all enter through Baptism. All who seek God with a sincere heart and who try in their actions to do his will may also achieve salvation."

For This Week:

I want to remember:

I want to put my faith into action by:

Questions to Explore

Prayer for the Week

*For in your benevolence you are pleased
to dwell in this house of prayer
in order to perfect us as the temple of the Holy Spirit,
supported by the perpetual help of your grace
and resplendent with the glory of a life acceptable to you.*

*Year by year you sanctify the Church, the Bride of Christ,
foreshadowed in visible buildings,
so that, rejoicing as the mother of countless children,
she may be given her place in your heavenly glory.*

(Common of the Dedication of a Church, Preface II, Outside the Church that was Dedicated, *Roman Missal*)

Twelfth Sunday in Ordinary Time

Scripture:

Job 38:1, 8–11
Psalm 107:23–24, 25–26, 28–29, 30–31
2 Corinthians 5:14–17
Mark 4:35–41

Focus:

THE POWER OF GOD

Reflection

Directions: *Here are a few situations in which evil reveals itself today: whole peoples without food, people living in dire poverty, governments torturing people, homeless people sleeping on the streets, corporate greed, child and spousal abuse. We say that God is all-powerful, and even has power over evil. Reflect on this and then answer this question: What does it mean to be Church and to believe in God's power in the face of the evil in these situations?*

Memorable People:

Saint Catherine of Siena (1347–1380), a Doctor of the Church and a mystical writer, commented in regard to reconciling a good and all-powerful God with the problem of evil in the world. She stated, "Everything comes from love, all is ordained for the salvation of [humanity], God does nothing without this goal in mind" (CathSienProv). Catherine taught about God's saving love that she so deeply experienced. Her feast day is April 29.

Did You Know?

Almost every Preface of the Eucharistic Prayer for Mass begins with the words, "It is truly right and just, our duty and our salvation, always and everywhere to give you thanks, Father most holy, through your beloved Son, Jesus Christ, . . ." (*Roman Missal*)

The Church Says:

God, who is all-powerful, created the world out of nothing to communicate and share divine goodness and love. Yet evil entered the world. Acting justly, God caused a flood, the Noah episode tells us, to destroy those who were evil and sinned. At the same time, God kept a faithful remnant. From the time of Abraham, the biblical story recounts God's power exercised in faithful love for the Israelites to free them from Egyptian bondage, and bring them to the promised land. The Bible further describes God's power in establishing a covenant, in expressing anger when the Israelites broke the covenant, and in continually calling the Israelites back in love.

God's power is manifested in Jesus Christ who came to save all people. Jesus is the Light of the world that no darkness or evil can overpower. Still evil is part of our daily life. No one part of the Christian message contains the whole answer to the question of evil. Catholics believe that creation is good. Though sin is at work in the world, God loves us and won't abandon us. Through the Holy Spirit the Church continues to proclaim God's love and goodness. As the Church community and through the celebration of the Sacraments, the Church stands ready to help turn back evil. No matter what evil befalls us, God's goodness and love will prevail in the end.

God could have created a perfect world, but chose instead to engage with us in the process of working for and moving toward a kingdom of justice, love, and peace.

For This Week:

I want to remember:

I want to put my faith into action by:

Questions to Explore	Prayer for the Week
	All-powerful and ever-living God, *in love you created me,* *I belong to you.* *When I am fearful,* *remind me of your presence.* *When I am weak,* *may I rely on your power.* *When I falter,* *help me cling to you, my rock.* *May I trust in your love* *no matter what evil I face.* *May my heart find peace and calm* *in knowing your love* *that impels me onward* *and surpasses all evil.* *Amen.*

Thirteenth Sunday in Ordinary Time

Scripture:

Wisdom 1:13–15, 2:23–24
Psalm 30:2, 4, 5–6, 11, 12, 13
2 Corinthians 8:7–9, 13–15
Mark 5:21–43

Focus:

 SANCTITY OF HUMAN LIFE

Reflection

Directions: *Imagine that you are the woman with the hemorrhage (What is draining the life out of you?) or the young girl (What appears to have died in you?). Write a prayer, poem, or meditation that reflects your desire to increase your faith in the power and authority of Jesus over death, his saving power to restore you to life.*

Questions

1. *What does Jesus' healing and life-giving power over the "worthless" members of our society evoke in you?*

2. *What moral implications flow from the sanctity of human life, particularly in terms of interdependence, the vulnerable and "worthless," charity and justice?*

Quotable Quotes:

Pope John Paul II, in his encyclical Evangelium Vitae *("The Gospel of Life"), reminds us that the* Didache, *the most ancient non-biblical Christian writing, exhorts us to a comprehensive perspective on the sacredness of human life: "There are two ways, a way of life and a way of death; there is a great difference between them. . . . In accordance with the precept of the teaching: You shall not kill . . . you shall not put a child to death by abortion nor kill it once it is born. . . . The way of death is this: . . . they show no compassion for the poor, they do not suffer with the suffering, they do not acknowledge their Creator, they kill their children and by abortion cause God's creatures to perish; they drive away the needy, oppress the suffering, they are advocates of the rich and unjust judges of the poor; they are filled with every sin." (Didache, I, 1; II, 1–2; V, 1 & 3)*

The Church Says:

All of the creation stories stress that God is the creator of life and we are to uphold the gift of life in its intrinsic goodness. The Old Testament prohibition against murder and killing is expanded by Jesus in the Sermon on the Mount (Matthew 5:21–22), where he warns against anger, hatred, and vengeance. Thus, the Church teaching on the sanctity of life reiterates the prohibition against violence and murder, but goes beyond, exhorting us to a comprehensive perspective, a holistic stance toward human life.

We are challenged to understand human life as a life of relationship, a gift of God, the fruit and sign of God's love. The unique relationship that Jesus has with each person empowers us to recognize the face of Christ in every human face. The value of every human life motivates us to transcend individualistic morality and comprehend the importance of interdependence within the human family and the whole of God's created world. This holistic attitude prompts us to act for the common good with profound respect for each person, particularly the vulnerable—the unborn, children, aged, ill, mentally and physically challenged, the poor and disenfranchised. Furthermore, the inherent goodness of all of life is what motivates us to act with charity, equality, and justice toward all.

For This Week:

I want to remember:

I want to put my faith into action by:

Questions to Explore

Prayer for the Week

Blessed be God, the creator of life,
  for you have made us out of goodness
  in your image and nature.
Blessed be Jesus, the redeemer of life,
  for your Resurrection bonds us to one another
  and frees us to live anew.
Blessed be the Spirit, sanctifier of life,
  for you empower us to see the face
  of the Risen One in each person.
Re-create, redeem, and restore us to holiness,
  exploding in our hearts
  a desire to love and care for
  your earth and all its creatures.
Amen.

Fourteenth Sunday in Ordinary Time

Scripture:

Ezekiel 2:2–5
Psalm 123:1–2, 2, 3–4
2 Corinthians 12:7–10
Mark 6:1–6

Focus:

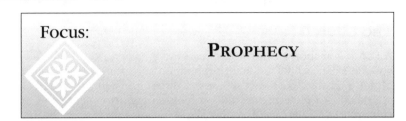

PROPHECY

Reflection

Directions: *Spend some quiet time reflecting on these questions:*
When have you experienced speaking the truth and then feeling the rejection or scorn of others?
What was it like for you?

Questions

1. *What was the role of the prophet as demonstrated in today's reading?*

2. *What is the role of the prophet today?*

3. *Who would you name as prophets of today?*

Memorable People:

Cesar Chavez spoke up for the rights of the United Farm Workers, a union he formed.
Martin Luther King, Jr., though not of the Catholic community, worked tirelessly for racial equality.
Dorothy Day worked with and for the poor.
Blessed Teresa of Calcutta worked with the outcasts and the dying.
Óscar Romero, Archbishop of San Salvador, was assassinated in 1979 as a result of standing with and for the poor.

Did You Know?

Old Testament patriarchs, prophets, and other significant figures are honored as Saints in the Church's liturgical tradition. Even if they have not been declared Saints by a formal canonical process, our worship includes them among the Saints because they are holy men and women who have looked forward to the coming of Christ.

The Church Says:

A prophet is one who is called by God to convey a message to God's people. The message was often a strong accusation or a stinging criticism concerning the people's infidelity, false worship, misplaced reliance on human ability, exploitation of the poor by the rich. And it may have been delivered to energize the people, to help them see a different future, to be more active in promoting God's rule or in announcing the new creation accomplished by God, the coming of the Messiah.

The Old Testament prophets accomplished three things: (1) They formed a people in the hope of Salvation and in the expectation of a new Covenant written on their hearts. (2) They proclaimed a radical Redemption of God's people from their unfaithfulness, a Redemption that ultimately would include all peoples. (3) They revealed by the conduct of their own lives the undying love of God for God's people.

Old Testament prophecy culminates in John the Baptist's statement that Jesus is the Lamb of God, the one anointed by the Holy Spirit for the threefold task of Priest, Prophet, and King. In the course of his ministry Jesus is prophetic, but unlike the prophets of the Old Testament, he is the fullness of God's Revelation, God's self-disclosure par excellence, the eternal Word made flesh.

For This Week:

I want to remember:

I want to put my faith into action by:

Questions to Explore

Prayer for the Week

O God, you have created, formed, and
appointed me to speak your Word of truth
and justice.
Keep your Word ever in my mind.
Open my lips that the words I speak may be
yours.
Give me a courageous heart to be steadfast
in my desire to give my all to you.
Help me walk the path of truth.
I ask this in Jesus' name.
Amen.

Fifteenth Sunday in Ordinary Time

Scripture:

Amos 7:12–15
Psalm 85:9–10, 11–12, 13–14
Ephesians 1:3–14
   [or (short form) 1:3–10]
Mark 6:7–13

Focus:

ELECTION AND MISSION

Reflection

Directions: *Picture yourself as a disciple following Jesus. You listen to his teachings, you see him calm the storm at sea, and you watch him cast out demons and heal the sick. Then Jesus looks at you and the other disciples and tells you to go out, preach repentance, cast out demons, and heal the sick.*

Questions

A. *Feelings I would have when Jesus sent me on this mission:*

B. *I would respond to Jesus by saying:*

Quotable Quote:

" A well-known passage describing God's chosen people is 1 Peter 2:9–10: *"But you are a chosen race, a royal priesthood, a holy nation, God's own people, in order that you may proclaim the mighty acts of him who called you out of darkness into his marvelous light. Once you were not a people, but now you are God's people; once you had not received mercy, but now you have received mercy.* "

Did You Know?

The word "apostle" means "one who is sent." The Apostles were sent out as witnesses to the Risen Christ. Saint Paul, seeing the Risen Christ in a vision, claimed himself to be an apostle.

The Church exists to "carry forth the Good News to every sector of the human race. . . . Proclamation, witness, teaching, sacraments, love of neighbor . . . are the means by which the one Gospel is transmitted . . . the essential elements of evangelization itself" (GDC 46).

The Church Says:

God elects, or chooses, people. This election is based on God's love and initiative, not on something done to earn it. The words "God's chosen," "God's anointed," and "God's people" all refer to the people God has chosen. These terms are used throughout the Bible. God chooses Israel, beginning with the call of Abraham and extending to Abraham's descendants. God established a covenant of love with the chosen people, the Israelites, who are claimed as God's "treasured possession" (Exodus 19:5), a people "living alone" (Numbers 23:9). Through gracious love, God faithfully calls the chosen people back into covenant relationship. The chosen people also have the responsibility to live according to this covenant relationship with God.

Jesus is God's elect one, the anointed one, the Christ who came to fulfill God's plan of Salvation. Through Jesus, God continues to choose new elect to continue Christ's mission. The chosen hear God's Word and must act on it. They are sent forth to further God's reign on Earth.

The Church exists to further Christ's mission for the renewal of the entire human family. Vatican Council II spoke of this mission, asserting: "The Church . . . travels the same journey as all humanity and shares the same earthly lot with the world: she is to be a leaven, and, as it were, the soul of human society in its renewal by Christ and transformation into the family of God" (GS 40).

Those who are baptized are claimed by the Church as God's elect. Each year on the First Sunday of Lent, the Church, acting in God's name, celebrates the election of catechumens who are ready for Baptism.

For This Week:

I want to remember:

I want to put my faith into action by:

Questions to Explore

Prayer for the Week

*God, blessed are you
  who has blessed us in Christ.
You chose us to be your holy people.
Claim us as your own.
May we walk in your ways.
May our hearts hear and follow your voice.
May we preach your Word of repentance
  in how we live and forgive.
May we be a healing presence
  through compassionate love and service.
Fill us with your love
  that we may show forth
  your light in our world.
Amen.*

Sixteenth Sunday in Ordinary Time

Scripture:

Jeremiah 23:1–6
Psalm 23:1–3, 3–4, 5, 6
Ephesians 2:13–18
Mark 6:30–34

Focus:

PASTORAL MINISTRY IN THE CHURCH

Reflection

Directions: *Spend some time reflecting upon this verse from today's Gospel: "He had compassion for them, because they were like sheep without a shepherd; and he began to teach them many things." Below make a list of those who in your experience fit this description. Then describe ways you would teach them about Jesus, either in words or in deeds.*

Questions

1. *What activities of the Church have you experienced or observed that correspond to these spheres of activity: Word, Worship, Community, and Service?*

2. *What feelings does the call to pastoral ministry evoke in you?*

Quotable Quote:

The late Joseph Cardinal Bernardin, who was the Archbishop of Chicago, wrote: *"Ministry involves activity. Usually a person does something for someone. The activity may be explicitly religious—prayer, liturgy, preaching—or it may be less explicitly religious yet grounded in faith and signifying hope in the coming kingdom of God—feeding the hungry, giving shelter to the homeless, working for justice, reconciliation and peace. Activity or function does not exhaust the meaning of ministry, however, nor does it essentially define ministry. Ministerial activity is ultimately directed toward establishing a life in communion with God and with one another, a way of life which manifests the kingdom of God in our midst."*
(*In Service of One Another, Pastoral Letter on Ministry, Archdiocese of Chicago, 1985, pp. 12–13*)

Did You Know?

The bishop of a diocese, at his installation ceremony, is given a crooked staff, a sign of his office as bishop. This crosier, also called a pastoral staff, resembles the shepherd's crook used to direct and guide the sheep of the flock. It symbolizes the bishop who in his ministry and person represents Christ, the Good Shepherd.

The Church Says:

Pastoral ministry refers to the service or ministry offered to the world, both within and beyond the Church community. The word "pastoral," an agricultural metaphor, brings to mind images of Jesus the shepherd, who guides, nourishes, protects, and reconciles his flock. While they are not mutually exclusive, it is helpful to think of the work of the Church in these four spheres of activity: (1) ministries that evolve around teaching and proclaiming the Word; (2) public activities involving worship, sacramental celebrations, and communal prayer; (3) activities that build up the community of the Church; and (4) those actions that serve those in need. Whatever specific and practical form it takes, pastoral ministry is designed to help people recognize and respond to the saving presence of God in this world. God reaches out to us time and again through the Spirit, inviting us to attain our true stature as God's children and our dignity as members of the Body of Christ. Thus, the Church is not to be confused with any political organization or secular society but is the People of God, brought together by a Shepherd—God—who reaches out to us through others in the Body of Christ.

For This Week:

I want to remember:

I want to put my faith into action by:

Questions to Explore

Prayer for the Week

God, you are our shepherd, guiding us through the members of this community and nourishing us with your Word of life. We are grateful that you have not abandoned us on our journey of faith. We seek to know you more clearly by feasting on your sacred Word, listening to the teaching of our leaders, and following the example of the members of this parish. Open our ears and heighten our imagination as we prepare to taste your food of life in the Eucharist. We ask this in the name of the Lord of justice.
Amen.

Seventeenth Sunday in Ordinary Time

Scripture:

2 Kings 4:42–44
Psalm 145:10–11, 15–16, 17–18
Ephesians 4:1–6
John 6:1–15

Focus:

UNITY OF THE CHURCH AND ECUMENISM

Reflection

Directions: *Consider a time when you were chosen to help solve or to be a part of the solution for a predicament. What was the problem? Who was involved? How were you involved? How did you respond when you were asked to be part of the solution? Imagine what would have happened if the little boy had refused to participate in the miracle. How did your response affect your solution?*

Did You Know?

The Greek word *oikoumene* means "the whole inhabited earth." In New Testament Greek, it originally meant "the household." Thus, in some of the Gospel parables of Jesus that speak of the "household steward" this term is used. Eventually it came to be applied to the whole household of the faithful, the Church, which extends throughout the world. This is the reason why we Catholics describe councils as "ecumenical," because they are comprised of bishops from around the globe. This is also the reason why the movement to heal the divisions between Christians through the world is described as "ecumenical."

The Church has experienced rifts from its very beginnings. Saint Paul wrote to censure divisions within the Body of Christ. Later, much more serious and lasting rifts called schisms occurred. The great schism of the eleventh century was between the Eastern Orthodox and the Western Catholics. Another rift is the Reformation of the sixteenth century between Roman Catholics, Protestants, and Anglicans.

The Church Says:

Catholics hold that the Church is characterized by unity because its very source is one. That source, the Trinity, is comprised of the Father, Son, and Holy Spirit, who are intimately united. Unity is a gift from above and is of the very essence of the household of faith, the People of God, who are bound together spiritually as one in Christ. Every Sunday in the liturgy when the Creed is prayed, Catholics proclaim their belief in the unity of the Church. Believers are called to maintain harmony and union among themselves. There is no place for prejudice or factionalism within the Church. Overcoming division is a pressing task because unity, not to be misunderstood as uniformity, is an essential mark of the Church.

For This Week:

I want to remember:

I want to put my faith into action by:

Questions to Explore

Prayer for the Week

*Good and gracious God,
gather all people to yourself.*

*Open our minds and hearts to see
what makes us one.*

*Remove all that divides us so that
with one voice we can sing
your praise and glory,
for you are the source of all creation.*

Amen.

Eighteenth Sunday in Ordinary Time

Scripture:

Exodus 16:2–4, 12–15
Psalm 78:3–4, 23–24, 25, 54
Ephesians 4:17, 20–24
John 6:24–35

Focus:

EUCHARISTIC CELEBRATION

Reflection

Directions: *In today's Gospel Jesus asserts that he is "the bread of life." In this statement he is not only saying that he is the Bread of Life in the Eucharist, but that he, in who he is, is the Bread of Life that provides the true nourishment we need to grow in our relationship with God. Allow yourself to think of a variety of ways Jesus is the Bread of Life for you. Some possibilities are written below. Add your own ideas.*

JESUS IS THE BREAD OF LIFE

- *By teaching us to forgive*
- *By coming to Zacchaeus's house*
-
-

- *By his faithfulness to God*
- *By his compassion for the poor*
-
-

The main parts of the Mass are listed below. Place an "x" by any of these parts with which you are not familiar. Talk about these with a Catholic friend.

INTRODUCTORY RITES
Entrance Chant
Greeting
Penitential Act
Gloria
Collect

LITURGY OF THE WORD
First Reading
Psalm
Second Reading
Alleluia
Gospel: Matthew, Mark, Luke, or John
Homily
Creed (Profession of Faith)
Prayer of the Faithful

LITURGY OF THE EUCHARIST
Preparation of the Altar and Gifts
Eucharistic Prayer
Acclamations
Holy, Holy, Holy
Memorial Acclamation
Amen

COMMUNION RITE
Lord's Prayer
Sign of Peace
Lamb of God
Reception of Communion

CONCLUDING RITES
Blessing and Dismissal

Quotable Quote:

St. Augustine (d. 430) preached: *"If you are the body and members of Christ, then it is your sacrament . . . placed on the table of the Lord; it is your sacrament that you receive. To which you are to respond 'Amen' ('Yes, it is true!') . . . For you hear the words, 'the Body of Christ' and respond 'Amen.' Be then a member of the Body of Christ that your Amen may be true."*

Did You Know?

Saint Tarsicius, the patron Saint of First Communicants, was a fourth-century young altar boy who took the Eucharist to Christians in prison. He risked his life during this time of persecution so that they could share in the Eucharistic meal. He eventually was stoned to death on one such mission. His feast day is August 15.

The Church Says:

Church believers have always gathered together to celebrate Jesus, the bread of life, in the Eucharistic celebration of Mass. From earliest times this celebration consisted of two main parts: the Liturgy of the Word and the Liturgy of the Eucharist. These two parts were described by Justin Martyr as early as A.D. 155, in a letter to the emperor. This basic structure of the Mass has remained to this day.

The Intoductory Rites provides for the assembly's gathering as a community of disciples. The Liturgy of the Word normally contains three readings, taken from the Old and New Testaments including the Gospel, and a Responsorial Psalm. The homily unfolds the meaning of the Scriptures for the lives of those gathered. The Prayer of the Faithful is prayed not only for the local Church, but for the universal Church and the world.

After the faithful bring forth the gifts of bread and wine, the solemn Eucharistic Prayer of thanksgiving recounting God's saving action throughout history is prayed. This prayer includes the narrative of Jesus' action at the Last Supper, the invocation of the Spirit, and prayers for the deceased and living members of the Church. The entire assembly proclaims "Amen!" at the conclusion of this prayer. The Communion Rite, Blessing, and Dismissal to go forth and live the Eucharist follow.

The Mass is a dialogue between the priest who leads the prayer, the various ministers, and the entire assembly. Music through hymns and acclamations is integral to the prayer of the Mass and aids the "full, active, and conscious participation" of all the faithful in the liturgy, called for by Vatican Council II (SC 14).

For This Week:

I want to remember:

I want to put my faith into action by:

Questions to Explore

Prayer for the Week

Gracious God, you provide
a rich feast for us.
You bid us come to your abundant table.
You feed our hearts as no other can.
When we are slow to respond to your invitation,
make our hunger for you grow.
Give us a hunger for nothing less than you.
As you feed us,
give us hearts that see
the hunger in our sisters and brothers.
Never let us be satisfied
until the rich and poor,
the happy and sad,
the prominent and forgotten,
share together at the table you set.
Amen.

Nineteenth Sunday in Ordinary Time

Scripture:

1 Kings 19:4–8
Psalm 34:2–3, 4–5, 6–7, 8–9
Ephesians 4:30–5:2
John 6:41–51

Focus:

EUCHARIST AS SACRIFICE AND SACRAMENT

Reflection

Directions: *Reflect on these three aspects of Eucharist found in Jesus' bread of life discourse, one at a time. When you are ready, write in the space provided your experiences and beliefs on the meaning of the Gospel teaching for your life.*

Divine Initiative: When have you felt the "pull" of God?

Jesus promises eternal life in his living bread: How does Jesus' teaching, "I am the living bread that came down from heaven. Whoever eats of this bread will live forever . . ." challenge your faith?

The bread is the flesh of Jesus sacrificed for the life of the world. What does this part of Jesus' teaching reveal to you: "The bread I will give is my flesh, for the life of the world"?

Did You Know?

Referring to the Eucharist, Saint Thomas Aquinas wrote: " . . . here Christ himself, the true God, is set before us as our food. What could be more wonderful than this? No other sacrament has greater healing power; through it sins are purged away, virtues are increased, and the soul is enriched with an abundance of every spiritual gift. It is offered in the Church for the living and the dead, so that what was instituted for the salvation of all may be for the benefit of all. Yet, in the end, no one can fully express the sweetness of this sacrament, in which spiritual delight is tasted at its very source, and in which we renew the memory of that surpassing love for us, which Christ revealed in his passion."

The Church Says:

The center of our faith as Christians is the free sacrifice of Christ on the Cross. In his outpouring of blood Christ ransomed sinners for all time. When we celebrate the Eucharist in the Catholic community, we not only recall what Jesus said and did at the Last Supper; we also connect intimately with the very heart of this central sacrifice of Jesus. Thus, the Church teaches that the Eucharist makes present to us the sacrifice of the cross. The abiding reality of Christ's Paschal sacrifice is present to us in the liturgy and we become present to it. This sacrifice is made present through the action of the Holy Spirit. As we are joined at the Eucharist to Christ's life and sacrifice on the Cross, our lives take on a new meaning and value. In fact, all who have gone before us and are in Heaven are joined with us in Christ through the Eucharist.

Furthermore, the Eucharist is a Sacrament. In words and ritual actions we celebrate and give thanks for our Redemption in Christ. In the Sacrament of the Eucharist, Christ is made present in the consecrated bread and wine, which becomes the Body and Blood of Jesus. Through the Sacrament of Eucharist, the Mass, Christ pours out his grace, bringing about our promised Salvation and eternal life.

For This Week:

I want to remember:

I want to put my faith into action by:

Questions to Explore

Prayer for the Week

Bread of Life,
nourish my body and spirit
as I seek to follow you in faith.
Loving Bread from Heaven,
console my weary heart
when hope seems lost and
my life seems a failure.
Bread of Eternal Life,
comfort me at my journey's end
that I might anticipate union with you
in everlasting joy.
May Jesus—bread and flesh given for the life
of the world—
be my seal and sacrament, sustaining me
as I journey to the mountain of God.
Amen.

Twentieth Sunday in Ordinary Time

Scripture:

Proverbs 9:1–6
Psalm 34:2–3, 10–11, 12–13, 14–15
Ephesians 5:15–20
John 6:51–58

The Continuing Presence of Jesus in the Eucharist

Reflection

Directions: *Name times when the family gathers for celebrations. Think about the elements that are part of your family celebrations, such as the place, the telling of stories, rituals, and food. Choose one family celebration and briefly describe it. Include your feelings as well as the activities.*

Did You Know?

Laws of the Church pertaining to Eucharist:
   Catholics are to participate in Mass every Sunday and holy day.
   Catholics fast from food and drink, except water (or medicine), for one hour before receiving the Eucharist.
   Catholics are to receive Eucharist at least once a year during the Easter Season.

The Eucharist is revered by Catholics who show their respect and worship of Jesus' presence by genuflecting or making a profound bow before the reserved Sacrament in the tabernacle. In addition, Catholics also show respect through Eucharistic adoration, when the consecrated host is carried in procession or displayed for veneration.

The Church Says:

The Church identifies four distinct ways in which Christ is present at Mass: in the person of the minister; in the Word proclaimed, since it is Christ who speaks; in the people gathered; in the Eucharistic species, the bread and wine. "Real Presence" is Christ's presence par excellence, since it is substantial, in the sense that Christ, whole and entire, God and man, becomes present. The bread and wine truly become Jesus' Body and Blood, and they remain his Body and Blood, even after the sacramental celebration is over.

The effects of Eucharistic grace are:

The Eucharist strengthens our union with Christ. What material food does for our bodies, Eucharist does for our spiritual life. Receiving Communion sustains, increases, and renews the grace obtained at Baptism by offering us intimate union with the Body and Blood of the Risen Christ.

The Eucharist also separates us from sin. Not only does it cleanse past repented sin; it assists us in avoiding future sins. The regular practice of receiving Communion helps the believer to grow in love and center more on Christ.

The Eucharist unites all those who receive it into one Body, the mystical Body of the Church. Believers are first incorporated into the Church at Baptism, and the Eucharist strengthens and renews this incorporation.

The Eucharist commits believers to the poor. Those who eat and drink the Body and Blood of Christ recognize him in the lowliest and needy.

The Eucharist compels us to strive for Christian unity. Painful divisions among Christians are made all the more poignant by the sacramental meal that should bind us as one.

For This Week:

I want to remember:

I want to put my faith into action by:

Questions to Explore	Prayer for the Week

Body of Christ, open me to
your whole Body—the People of God.

Blood of Christ, cleanse me
from all sin and wrongdoing
both inside and out.

I ask that your presence in the Eucharist
be a sign to me
of our Covenant of love,
won through sacrifice and suffering.

May the Eucharist inspire me
to become a sign of your presence
in the world
as I make myself present to others.

Amen.

Twenty-first Sunday in Ordinary Time

Scripture:

Joshua 24:1–2a, 15–17, 18b
Psalm 34:2–3, 16–17, 18–19, 20–21, 22–23
Ephesians 5:21–32 or 5:21, 25–32
John 6:60–69

Focus:

FAITH

Reflection

Directions: With about 2000 years from the time of Jesus to the present, for many of us it is not difficult to accept that Jesus is the chosen one sent by God to redeem us. Yet believing in Jesus does make demands on us. Reflect on your life and respond to the following:

1. *What does being a follower of Jesus demand of you?*

2. *What are some of the hard choices you have had to make in being a disciple of Jesus?*

Reflect on the history of your faith in Jesus and answer these questions:

1. *Who first told you about Jesus and what were your thoughts about him then?*

2. *Were there times when you turned away from Jesus? If so, what prompted this decision?*

3. *How has your belief in Jesus changed from "knowing about" Jesus to being in a personal relationship with Jesus? What brought about this transformation?*

Memorable People:

Leonard Bernstein's 1971 composition, "Mass," was meant to honor John Kennedy and Pope John XXIII. In this theater piece for singers, players, and dancers, patterned on our Catholic liturgy, the celebrant presides over a noisy, confusing assembly representing the modern world. This presider first expresses his faith, then loses his faith, and at the end regains faith through the example of an innocent child.

Did You Know?

The Hebrew word for faith, *aman*, from which the word *"amen"* comes, implies something "solid" or "trustworthy" to which we pledge our loyalty. Faith is thus understood as a trusting belief in a person.

In the Rite of Baptism for Children the Church prays that parents, who are the first teachers of their childin the ways of faith, will be "the best of teachers, bearing witness to the faith by what they say and do."

The Church Says:

Faith invites us into a relationship of love with God. God is fully revealed through Jesus, who embodies divine love and communicates that love to us by his life and mission, and in his suffering, Death, and Resurrection. Faith is a free gift of God that invites our free response. The gift of faith is, therefore, a relationship through which we trust the truth of that which has been revealed in Jesus Christ, and handed down to us through the Church. This heritage of faith is entrusted to the whole Church. Catholics understand this sacred deposit of faith is contained in both Sacred Scripture and Sacred Tradition.

Faith offers a sense of assurance in a broken world through its specific content arising from the person of Jesus Christ. Vatican Council II emphasized Saint Augustine's observation that Catholics can be confident in the content of faith due to the sensus fidei, the supernatural appreciation of the faith of the whole Church. The council makes three points to support this understanding: the content of faith is about matters of universal faith and morals; it is stated under the guidance of the teaching authority of the Church; and it is given to us by God.

All people have a desire for God. This desire may be ignored or rejected due to ignorance, indifference, materialism, bad example, or sin. Those who respond to the gift of faith and who place their trust in God have a new understanding and vision of life. They are supported within a community of believers, and through the guidance of the Holy Spirit participate with the entire Church in the mission of Christ.

For This Week:

I want to remember:

I want to put my faith into action by:

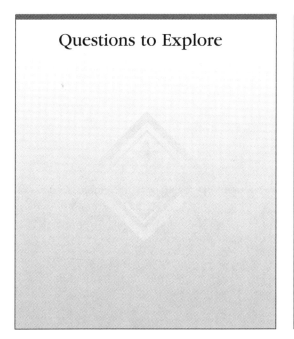

Questions to Explore

Prayer for the Week

God, I thank you for the faith you have given me.
Help me guard and protect this gift of faith
through love of others
and a commitment to prayer.
Strengthen my faith in times of fear and doubt.
Purify my faith in times of suffering and distress.
Keep my eyes fixed on you
that my heart will know you are truly
the One who brings me life.
You have graciously gifted me
with this community of faith
to support and nourish the seed of faith
you have planted in my soul.
May I walk and live in faithful relationship with you.
Empower me to support and encourage
your gift of faith in others.
Amen.

Twenty-second Sunday in Ordinary Time

Scripture:

Deuteronomy 4:1–2, 6–8
Psalm 15:2–3, 3–4, 5–6
James 1:17–18, 21b–22, 27
Mark 7:1–8, 14–15, 21–23

Focus:

PRINCIPLES OF MORALITY

Reflection

Directions: *Rewrite the Ten Commandments in a positive style. You might find it helpful to begin each Commandment with the words "You shall . . ." Below each Commandment list several ways to act on that Law of God.*

1. *I am the LORD your God: you shall not have strange gods before me.*
   You shall . . .

2. *You shall not take the name of the LORD your God in vain.*
   You shall . . .

3. *Remember to keep holy the LORD's Day.*
   You shall . . .

4. *Honor your father and your mother.*
   You shall . . .

5. *You shall not kill.*
   You shall . . .

6. *You shall not commit adultery.*
   You shall . . .

7. *You shall not steal.*
   You shall . . .

8. *You shall not bear false witness against your neighbor.*
   You shall . . .

9. *You shall not covet your neighbor's wife.*
   You shall . . .

10. *You shall not covet your neighbor's goods.*
    You shall . . .

Memorable People:

Martha and Mary have traditionally been regarded as symbols of action and contemplation, respectively (see Luke 10:38–42). To appreciate the moral life, one must "sit at the feet of the Master" and contemplate his teaching and all that is good. This contemplation, however, issues forth in action throughout life. The interplay of these images of Martha and Mary is captured by Patrick Henry Ryan, a Trappist monk at the Abbey of the Genesee, in his poem "Mary Sat." He writes: "Martha stood/ but Mary sat / and the sitting / led within / the things / that need two feet / to love / so peaceful / Martha / could not leave / her sister / all alone."

The Church Says:

The natural law is inscribed in our hearts because it is woven into the very fabric of creation. This natural law is knowable and understandable. In seeking to uncover this natural law, the Church centers her teaching around these eight themes: the Holy Spirit, grace, the Beatitudes, sin and forgiveness, human virtues, Theological Virtues, the Great Commandment, and the Church itself.

Furthermore, the Church teaches that the end does not justify the means, because a good intention cannot transform an intrinsically bad or immoral act into something that is morally good.

Each Catholic has the responsibility to inform his or her conscience to develop the inner disposition of holiness aimed at imitating Christ. Conscience is shaped by experiences, values, and symbols guided by the community of faith and oriented toward the kingdom realities of creation, freedom, covenant, love, incarnation, death, and resurrection. Morality is primarily concerned with human freedom, resulting from God's loving plan that guides all creation toward authentic fulfillment. Because the goal of the moral life for the Christian is happiness with God, Christian morality is concerned with grace—God's gift of friendship extended to humankind. Although sinful, we are graced, that is, gifted with the Covenant relationship with God through Jesus.

For This Week:

I want to remember:

I want to put my faith into action by:

Questions to Explore

  ### Prayer for the Week

Purify us, O God,
cleanse us from within,
that we might be people of light for the world.

Inscribe your Laws of love
into our fleshy hearts and
remove all that is sinful,
freeing us to imitate the way of Jesus.

Amen.

Twenty-third Sunday in Ordinary Time

Scripture:

Isaiah 35:4–7a
Psalm 146:7, 8–9, 9–10
James 2:1–5
Mark 7:31–37

Focus:

CATHOLIC SOCIAL TEACHING

Reflection

Directions: *Recall an encounter you have had with a disadvantaged person, such as the homeless, a person with AIDS, a physically disabled or disfigured person, or a television report you watched on such people. Describe your reaction to the encounter or viewing. Is there anything you wish you had done differently? Why?*

Recall an encounter you have had with a rich and famous person, or a television report you watched on such a person. Describe your reaction to the encounter or viewing. Is there anything you wish you had done differently? Why?

Questions

In one column make a list of the criteria used by our society to determine if someone is successful. In a second column make a list of the criteria given to us by God as guidelines for living a Christian life. Compare the two lists. Note the similarities and differences. Based on your lists and discussion, what conclusions might be made?

SOCIETY'S CRITERIA   CHRISTIAN CRITERIA

Did You Know?

The following are some of the chief statements regarding the Church's social teachings:

Rerum novarum was written in 1891 by Pope Leo XIII. It is a foundational pronouncement for the cause of the poor and oppressed of the world.

Mater et magistra and *Pacem in terris,* both written by Pope John XXIII, also articulate the Church's concern for the poor and the oppressed and the need to address the causes of poverty and oppression. *Gaudium et spes* was promulgated by the Second Vatican Council.

Populorum progressio was written by Pope Paul VI. *Sollicitudo rei socialis, Laborem exercens,* and *Centesimus annus* (written to mark the centenary of *Rerum novarum*) were written by Pope John Paul II.

Other pastoral documents have been written by the Conference of Bishops of various countries.

The Church Says:

God entrusts Earth to us. It does not belong to us, but to God, and we are called to be good stewards of it and all its resources. The resources of the planet are meant for the common good of the whole human race. The right to private property does not invalidate God's original gift of Earth to the whole of humanity. By work or by inheritance private property is acquired; however, the universal distribution of goods remains fundamental. Civil authority has a duty to regulate legitimate production of goods and services for the benefit of the common good. Economically, respect for human dignity requires the practice of the virtues of temperance and justice, and the practice of solidarity. Temperance moderates our attachments to this world's goods. Justice preserves our neighbor's rights and renders to them what is their due. The practice of solidarity regulates one's behavior in concert with others to benefit those less fortunate. As good stewards we must respect the integrity of God's creation. All animals, plants, and mineral resources must be used with respect for what God has created. As a Church we are concerned with the temporal aspects of the common good precisely because these aspects are ordered to God, our ultimate end. Thus, the Church makes moral judgments regarding economic and social matters.

For This Week:

I want to remember:

I want to put my faith into action by:

Questions to Explore

Prayer for the Week

All-powerful and ever-loving God,
  we sing your praise forever
  and give thanks in all we do,
  through Jesus Christ, your Son.
He proclaimed to all a message of justice and peace,
  a message that lives on in our midst
  as a task for us today
  and a promise for tomorrow.
We thank you for your blessings of the past,
  and we ask your help for the justice
  we must yet achieve.
Strengthen us as we struggle
  to bring your justice to all people.
We ask this in the name of Jesus our brother.
Amen.

Twenty-fourth Sunday in Ordinary Time

Scripture:

Isaiah 50:5–9a
Psalm 116:1–2, 3–4, 5–6, 8–9
James 2:14–18
Mark 8:27–35

Focus:

WHAT IS A PROFESSION OF FAITH?

Reflection

Directions: *Today's Gospel passage from Mark contains Peter's famous profession of faith, "You are the Messiah." Over time various aspects of our belief in who Jesus is unfolds. List as many beliefs about who Jesus is for you in the space below.*

Jesus, I believe you are . . .
- *the Holy One of God*
- *the Bread of Life*
-
-

- *the one who teaches forgiveness*
-
-
-

Questions

Believing in God is not just a mental acceptance of truths about God. Believing in God also impels us to reflect our belief in how we live.

What understandings about God are difficult for you to accept?

In what ways do you live differently because of your belief in God?

Quotable Quote:

> *"So faith by itself, if it has no works, is dead. But if someone will say,*
> *'You have faith and I have works.' Show me your faith apart from your works,*
> *and I by my works will show you my faith." (James 2:17–18)*

Did You Know?

The early Church during the days of persecution referred to the Apostles' Creed as the *Symbolum Apostolicum.* An ancient source, Tyrannius Rufinus's *Commentarius* in *Symbolum Apostolorum* (A.D. 404), states that in the days of the martyrs, "the creed or symbol functioned as a password, a sign or token whereby members of the Christian community could recognize one another."

The Church Says:

Peter confessed his belief that Jesus is the Christ, which means the "Anointed One" or the Messiah. In the first centuries after Christ the Church wrestled with articulating the central beliefs of the Church. These beliefs are formulated in a creed by which the entire Church professes its faith in God. The term "creed" is from the Latin credo, which means "I believe," with the sense of "putting one's heart into, or giving oneself to, someone or something" in a committed way.

The creed contains beliefs revealed by God about what God has done through Jesus Christ by the power of the Holy Spirit. Primarily two creeds are used by the Church today. The Apostles' Creed, from the third century, begins with the words "I believe," and is personally confessed, usually in question and answer form, at baptism. The Nicene-Constantinople Creed (381), named for the Church councils that articulated the beliefs named, is professed by the assembly at liturgy on Sundays and important feasts. It begins, "I believe." The ancient Latin saying, Lex orandi, lex credendi ("the law of prayer is the law of faith"), articulates the truth that in authentic worship the way the Church prays points to and expresses true beliefs.

Faith is an active response to God's Revelation in the world. Believing Christians are sent forth into the world as living witnesses of the Good News of Salvation in Jesus Christ. The Second Vatican Council taught: "All Christians by example of their lives and the witness of the word . . . have an obligation to manifest the new [person] which they put on at baptism (AG11). This witnessing is how the Church hands on the faith in words and deeds.

For This Week:

I want to remember:

I want to put my faith into action by:

Questions to Explore

Prayer for the Week

Glory and praise to you, my God,
the God whom women and men of faith
have believed in for centuries.
Deepen my belief in you,
the one who created me,
the one who gives me the gift of faith,
the one who teaches my heart your ways.
Keep my heart directed toward you
in times of suffering and challenge.
Open me to the depth and power
of the way of life Christ proclaimed.
Make me sensitive to the inner promptings
of your Holy Spirit.
May I be a faithful witness of the Good News
of your saving action in all I do.
Amen.

Twenty-fifth Sunday in Ordinary Time

Scripture:

Wisdom 2:12, 17–20
Psalm 54:3–4, 5, 6–8
James 3:16–4:3
Mark 9:30–37

Focus:

THE CALL
TO SERVICE

Reflection

Directions: *Imagine that you are a follower of Jesus and he speaks these words to you: "The Son of Man is to be betrayed into human hands, and they will kill him . . . " Write down your feelings. Then list the implications of this statement in your life today.*

Questions

1. *In the light of the Gospel, Matthew 20:1–16, what is your definition of servant? Service?*

2. *Describe someone you know who has achieved greatness because of his or her attitude of service.*

Quotable Quote:

" The Second Vatican Council proclaimed: *"The Church is not motivated by an earthly ambition but is interested in one thing only—to carry on the work of Christ under the guidance of the Holy Spirit, for he came into the world to bear witness to the truth, to save and not to judge, to serve and not to be served"* (GS 3). "

Did You Know?

Today the Church is frequently seen as a supplementary service provider. But in medieval Europe it was the sole source of medical help, care for the poor and travelers, and the only educational resource.

The Church Says:

Just as Jesus came to serve others and not to be served, all who would follow him are called to humble service. This poses a challenge, for we desire affirmation and seek self-aggrandizement. Yet because God raised our self-emptying Christ above all others, our true measure of greatness is honed as we assume the same servant attitude of Christ.

Sacred Scriptures describe the role of the servant in a variety of terms and images. All images underline the scriptural idea that being a servant implies single-minded devotion. As we place our allegiance with God in Jesus, we will open our hearts to assume the call of service.

In Baptism we are incorporated into Christ and called to this life of service. This call to service implies action. Works of justice and mercy, actions for peace, and compassionate kindness are some of the ways we serve others. Each of us is challenged to respond to Jesus' call by a life of service based upon our unique gifts and the circumstances in which we live.

For This Week:

I want to remember:

I want to put my faith into action by:

Questions to Explore

Prayer for the Week

O God, we seek your ways of wisdom.
We search for ways to offer ourselves to you
as servants of justice, truth, and love.
Fill us with the compassion of Jesus.
May his suffering and Death inspire us
when we are tired, overwhelmed,
and in the midst of our struggles.
May your Spirit open our eyes to
those in need who come into our lives each day.
Help us carry on the works of Christ
in our world today.
In Jesus' name we humbly pray.

Amen.

Twenty-sixth Sunday in Ordinary Time

Scripture:

Numbers 11:25–29
Psalm 19:8, 10, 12–13, 14
James 5:1–6
Mark 9:38–43, 45, 47–48

Focus:

CATHOLIC SOCIAL TEACHING

Reflection

Directions: *Slowly and deliberately read the last portion of the Gospel, Mark 9:43–48. Think of actions or lack of actions that might be the causes of sin.*

Paraphrase this portion of the Gospel in your own words.

Questions

1. *How do the Scriptures, the Commandments of love, and the teachings of the Church provide a source of determining right from wrong in moral decision making?*

2. *What role does conscience play in your moral decision making?*

3. *How do your decisions have a ripple effect on the lives of others, even those you will never meet?*

Quotable Quote:

The Second Vatican Council asserted that remuneration for work should guarantee a person "the opportunity to provide a dignified livelihood for self and family on the material, social, cultural and spiritual level" (GS 67).

Memorable People:

The Catholic Worker is the name of both a newspaper and movement dedicated to the improvement of the social order. The newspaper was established by Dorothy Day (1897–1980), a convert to Catholicism who was influenced by the French intellectual Peter Maurin (1877–1949). "As a social movement the Catholic Worker comprises communities of workers who are committed to practicing the works of mercy. . . .In addition to staffing houses of hospitality to assist poor people, workers engaged in direct and public actions to arouse the consciences of others and to resist the militarist state and materialist society."

The Church Says:

Everything economically is ordered first of all to the service of persons and to the entire community. Profit cannot be the ultimate end of economic activity and the individual cannot be subordinated to the collective organization of production. Anything that reduces humans to nothing more than a means of profit enslaves persons. Economic activity sometimes brings into play competing interests. The resolution of conflicts arising from economic activity should come about through negotiation that respects the rights and duties of each facet of the social partnership between business enterprises, representatives of wage earners such as trade unions, and public authorities. We believe that access to employment and to professions must be available and open to everyone without discrimination. This includes both men and women, healthy and disabled, natives and immigrants. A just wage should be given for work performed. This just wage must take into account the role and productivity of each, relevant economic factors in each person's employment, and the common good.

For This Week:

I want to remember:

I want to put my faith into action by:

Questions to Explore

Prayer for the Week

*May the Lord enlighten us with the truth
of the Gospel,
May we come to recognize Christ's face in
every human being,
May we be strengthened with courage to
work for justice.
We ask this through Christ our Lord. Amen.*

Twenty-seventh Sunday in Ordinary Time

Scripture:

Genesis 2:18–24
Psalm 128:1–2, 3, 4–5, 6
Hebrews 2:9–11
Mark 10:2–16
  [or (short form) 10:2–12]

Focus:

MARRIAGE, DIVORCE, AND ANNULMENT

Reflection

Directions:

1. *Make a list of characteristics of marital love that you have experienced or observed.*

2. *From your list make specific statements characterizing God's love for all people. Use the format, "God's love is . . ."*

3. *Then respond to the following questions:*

   In what ways does God's love "grace" your marital relationship and/or friendships?

   What gifts do you bring to your relationships?

   How does God's faithful love bring about miracles in ordinary relationships?

Memorable People:

Saint Margaret of Scotland (1050–1093) found time to be a wife, queen, mother, and Saint. Raising her six children and working with her husband, King Malcolm, Margaret found time every day to rise early to prepare breakfast for the hundreds of beggars that gathered outside the castle each day. Her feast day is November 16.

Did You Know?

The Catholic tradition of giving a ring to one's spouse at the wedding is said to originate in the symbolism of a circle, a ring. It has no beginning and no end, and thus is a sign of undivided, total giving that cannot, like a circle, be broken.

The Church Says:

God created humans male and female with a sexuality that is good. God draws men and women together to give themselves in total partnership to each other and become one flesh. God's will is for a lasting union between spouses.

Marriage is one of the Seven Sacraments of the Church. The couple are the ministers of the Sacrament, ministering God's love in deep personal ways one to the other. Catholic marriage takes place before a priest and two witnesses. When all the requirements are present at the time of the marriage, the marriage is insoluble. Though sin results in discord, infidelity, hatred, and jealousy, Christ gives couples grace through his Passion, Death, and Resurrection. Divorce is not an option if the marriage results from the free act of the spouses and is consummated.

An annulment, a declaration by the Church that what appeared to be a marriage is invalid because an essential element was missing from the beginning, may be obtained for one of three reasons. One or more of twelve impediments or a lack of the appropriate form of marriage may have been present. A marriage resulting from these two situations can be declared null in a somewhat simple Church procedure. A lack of full internal consent by one or both of the spouses must go through a structured judicial process of the local diocesan tribunal. Because all situations are different, it is best to consult a priest or pastoral minister trained for annulment work.

The Church provides a preparation process for couples desiring marriage. Two kinds of couples' retreats— Marriage Encounter, to help couples improve their communication patterns, and Retrouvaille, for marriages in difficulty—are available in most dioceses.

For This Week:

I want to remember:

I want to put my faith into action by:

Questions to Explore

Prayer for the Week

Creator of love, it is you who first loved us,
  making it possible for us to love one another,
  in spite of our human weaknesses.
Bless the love between couples everywhere.
Embrace them, sending your Spirit
  of gentleness and affection,
  of joy and playfulness,
  of tenderness and compassion,
  that through the love of mere humans
  you might renew the world.
In all of our relationships
  grace us with the willingness
  to give and forgive.
Amen.

Twenty-eighth Sunday in Ordinary Time

Scripture:

Wisdom 7:7–11
Psalm 90:12–13, 14–15, 16–17
Hebrews 4:12–13
Mark 10:17–30

Focus:

WORD OF GOD/
REVELATION

Reflection

Directions: *Reflect upon these lines from the Gospel, Mark 10:17–30, and jot down your insights after each:*

" . . . what must I do to inherit eternal life?" (Mark 10:17)

"You lack one thing; go, sell what you own, and give the money to the poor, and you will have treasure in heaven."
(Mark 10:21)

"Then come, follow me." (Mark 10:21)

"He went away grieving." (Mark 10:22)

" . . . how hard it is to enter the kingdom of God! It is easier for a camel to go through the eye of a needle than for someone who is rich to enter the kingdom of God." (Mark 10: 24–25)

"For mortals it is impossible, but not for God; for God all things are possible." (Mark 10–27)

Questions

1. *How would you describe the radical invitation of Jesus? What does this mean for your life?*

2. *What is the reward for this radical commitment?*

3. *In what ways does this Word of God "cut through" your apathy and the routine manner you live the faith?*

Did You Know?

For the first reliable fountain that brought running water into the heart of Siena, an Italian city high in the hills, the artist Jacopo della Quercia (d. 1438) sculpted Mary, the Mother of God, holding the Christ child. They are surrounded by the figures representing Wisdom, Hope, Fortitude, Prudence, Justice, Humility, Temperance, and Faith, bounded at its far ends by women with children, symbolizing earthly and divine Charity (HistItal 184). It is as if these virtues of the believer's life flow from or out of the refreshing and life-giving waters of revelation given in Jesus by his mother, our mother Mary, symbol of the Church itself, all held and containedby the love of God.

The Church Says:

Jesus is the total Revelation of God and of God's love for humankind. He is the eternal Word, the self-communication of God to humanity. God invites us to respond to this love, yet we are free to accept or reject God's Revelation in Jesus. Our response is a free assent of our whole person: mind, heart, and body.

We do not act alone in accepting God's Revelation. Faith is born, nourished, and sustained in the community of believers, which is of the Church. What the Apostles received from Christ, they handed on to later generations. This is a living message, the Good News of Jesus given as a gift to the Church through the Holy Spirit. God's Revelation is communicated chiefly through, but is not limited to, Sacred Tradition and Sacred Scripture. Both Scripture and Tradition function as the source for us in understanding and living the Word of God—God's Revelation.

For This Week:

I want to remember:

I want to put my faith into action by:

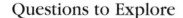

Questions to Explore	Prayer for the Week
	O Wisdom of the Ages, *O Revelation of God,* *Jesus the Christ,* *anoint us with your gifts* *of wisdom, truth, and light.* *Oh, that we might love your Word* *which cuts through all deceit* *and reveals the heart of truth.* *Fill us with love for the riches that* *never fade.* *Grant us everlasting life in you.* *Amen.*

Twenty-ninth Sunday in Ordinary Time

Scripture:

Isaiah 53:10–11
Psalm 33:4–5, 18–19, 20, 22
Hebrews 4:14–16
Mark 10:35–45
[or (short form) 10:42–45]

Focus:

REDEMPTION BY CHRIST'S SUFFERING

Reflection

Directions: Spend some quiet time pondering these questions:

What are James and John asking Jesus for?

What do you think James and John understood the mission of Jesus to be by their request?

What is Jesus saying to James and John when he says, "You do not know what you are asking"?

Quotable Quote:

"In Masses honoring the Most Sacred Heart of Jesus, the Church prays: *"[F]or raised up high on the Cross, [Christ] gave himself up for us with a wonderful love and poured out Blood and water from his pierced side, the wellspring of the Church's Sacraments, so that, won over to the open Heart of the Savior, all might draw water joyfully from the springs of salvation."*
(Preface, The Most Sacred Heart of Jesus, *Roman Missal*)

Did You Know?

Pontius Pilate unknowingly proclaimed an article of faith when he stated, "Behold the man!" This is the most Christian of titles for Jesus. This entire mystery—Incarnation, Resurrection, and Ascension—unfolds as Jesus journeys among us, the eternal Word become flesh, in order to save us. John the Baptist proclaims, "Behold the Lamb of God who takes away the sins of the world," which is prayed or sung as part of the Communion Rite of the Mass.

The Church Says:

Jesus preached the healing of God and died proclaiming God's forgiveness and love. The profound mystery of the Cross and Resurrection of Jesus Christ stands as the focal point of faith.

In his life, suffering, Death, Resurrection, and Ascension, Jesus did for us what we cannot do for ourselves, he redeemed us from sin and death. Humanity has been rescued by God's own loving initiative in Jesus Christ. One person, Jesus Christ, accomplishes Salvation, achieved for everyone without exception. Jesus Christ accomplishes the unique and definitive Salvation precisely because his is both fully human and fully divine in one person. He accomplishes our Redemption from sin and death by his own free participation in God's plan of Salvation. The Redemption achieved by the initiative of God in Christ can be perceived only through the eyes of faith. We are redeemed because God loves us and calls us to be in communion with the Godhead.

For This Week:

I want to remember:

I want to put my faith into action by:

Questions to Explore

Prayer for the Week

*We adore you, O Christ,
and we bless you,
because by your holy cross
you have redeemed the world.
Amen.*

Thirtieth Sunday in Ordinary Time

Scripture:

Jeremiah 31:7–9
Psalm 126:1–2, 2–3, 4–5, 6
Hebrews 5:1–6
Mark 10:46–52

Focus:

HOLY ORDERS AND THE COMMON PRIESTHOOD OF THE BAPTIZED

Reflection

Directions:

1. *Experience is often effectively expressed in images. Today's Scriptures use a variety of images to portray God's actions including: gathering people from the ends of the earth, bringing people back to their homeland, providing a level path, for walking, leading to a stream of water, and giving sight to the blind. Describe the images that express how God has acted with care toward you.*

2. *Jesus Christ is the one High Priest. All the baptized share in this priesthood of Christ. Below are listed some understandings of the meaning of sharing in Christ's priesthood. Add your additional understandings of the meaning of this priesthood of all believers.*

   THE PRIESTHOOD OF CHRIST INVOLVES:
   - *total self-gift*
   - *complete obedience to God*
   - *faithful service*
   - *chosen by God*

Memorable People:

Archbishop Óscar Romero of El Salvador was assassinated in 1980 for his work with the poor. His story is portrayed in the movie *Romero*.

Joseph Cardinal Bernardin, Archbishop of Chicago who died November 14, 1996, publicly forgave the man who falsely accused him of grave sin in the news media.

Pope Saint John XXIII is well known for convening Vatican Council II in 1962, and for his peace encyclical, *Pacem in Terris*.

Stephen, one of the original seven deacons, was stoned to death (Acts 6:1–6 and 7:54–60).

Did You Know?

For liturgical ministry priests wear the alb (the white garment of Baptism), a chasuble (a decorative overgarment), and stole (a narrow band of cloth over the shoulders). Bishops wear these vestments with the addition of a miter (a pointed hat, symbolizing their office of ruling) and walk with a crosier, or shepherd's staff, showing their role as shepherd of God's people. Deacons wear albs, dalmatics (similar to a chasuble but closed on the sides), and stoles over one shoulder.

The Church Says:

Christ, chosen by God and obedient to God's will, is the one great High Priest who offered the perfect sacrifice of himself for the Salvation of all people. All who are chosen for Baptism in Christ share in the one priesthood of Christ. The faithful exercise their baptismal priesthood through a life of faith, hope, and love manifested in their particular call and obligations of life.

Bishops, priests, and deacons who receive the Sacrament of Holy Orders are chosen to share in Christ's ministerial priesthood, serving the common priesthood of all believers by assisting in unfolding the baptismal grace of all Christians.

In the early Church both a charismatic leadership based on Gifts of the Spirit and an ordained leadership with the three ministries of bishop, priest, and deacon developed. From the time of the Apostles the Church has continued to ordain people for these three ministries.

Bishops (the episcopate, "overseers") are consecrated to sanctify, teach, and rule as Christ's representatives. Together with the Pope, the Bishop of Rome, they continue Christ's work of shepherding God's people. Priests (presbyterate), signed with a special character to act in the person of Christ, are coworkers sharing in the bishop's ministry. Priests preach the Gospel, celebrate Sacraments, preside at liturgy, and shepherd the faithful. Deacons (diaconate, "servants") assist bishops and priests in the celebration of the Eucharist, the proclamation of the Gospel and preaching, presiding at funerals, weddings, and Baptisms, and in charitable outreach to those in need. Baptized men receive the Sacrament of Holy Orders from a validly ordained bishop through the laying on of hands and the bishop's consecratory prayer.

For This Week:

I want to remember:

I want to put my faith into action by:

Questions to Explore

Prayer for the Week

God, we praise and thank you for the gift
of your beloved Son,
our great High Priest.
Thank you for choosing us
to share in Christ's priesthood.
Give us the willingness
to respond in faithful obedience to you,
to give of ourselves for others,
to spend our lives at the service of your kingdom.
Make us your instruments
in our homes and places of work.
Bless all of the Church's leaders
with fidelity to their call.
May we all work together until that day
when your kingdom is fully realized.
Amen.

Thirty-first Sunday in Ordinary Time

Scripture:

Deuteronomy 6:2–6
Psalm 18:2–3, 3–4, 47, 51
Hebrews 7:23–28
Mark 12:28–34

Focus:

COMMAND TO LOVE GOD AND NEIGHBOR

Reflection

Directions: *List some practical changes you wish to undertake to better obey the Commandment, "Hear, O Israel: the Lord our God, the Lord is one; you shall love the Lord your God with all your heart, and with all your soul, and with all your mind, and with all your strength. . . . You shall love your neighbor as yourself."*

Loving God wholeheartedly means that I will . . .

Loving my neighbor, who is loved by God, means that I will . . .

Questions

1. *How does the love for God and neighbor bless or sanctify our daily living?*

2. *Describe an experience of the transforming power of God's love.*

3. *In what ways can loving God by loving our neighbor bring about the kingdom?*

Quotable Quote:

❝ *The whole concern of doctrine and its teaching must be directed to the love that never ends. Whether something is proposed for belief, for hope or for action, the love of our Lord must always be made accessible, so that anyone can see that all the works of perfect Christian virtue spring from love and have no other objective than to arrive at love.* ❞
(RC, Preface, 10)

The Church Says:

We cannot claim to love God without that love manifesting itself in our love for others. God's love, first expressed in creation, expressed itself in a covenant of love between the one God and the chosen people of Israel. The covenant love of God is embodied and fulfilled in the life, teaching, and saving action of Jesus the Christ. His self-sacrifice for us, the Paschal Mystery, unlocked the font of grace by which we are born again as brothers and sisters of one another and witnesses to the world of the great love of God.

Remember the refrain of the song, "They will know we are Christians by our love." This mission of love, manifested in loving God by loving our neighbor, has the power to transform human society into the kingdom of harmony, peace, and justice, which Christ came to announce. Through the Sacraments, especially the Eucharist, we are empowered to witness God's love, for we are transformed more closely into the image of Christ. Thus, the Church teaches that the love of God and neighbor is the soul of sanctification, the soul of the apostolate, and the source of prayer. It is the rationale for all that the Church teaches and does.

For This Week:

I want to remember:

I want to put my faith into action by:

Questions to Explore

Prayer for the Week

Hear our prayer, O God of Love, that we might learn to love the neighbor who is on the outside of our inner circle: the unlovable, the odd-looking, homeless, deformed, strange neighbors we pass by each day who cry to us for a look of love, a smile, a helping hand.

Give us compassion to forgive the neighbor who has wronged, hurt, disagreed with us, or disparaged us. For we believe that divine love transforms even our stubborn hearts.

Give us the courage to lay down our lives for the neighbor who is sick, dying, grieving, and forgotten, as Jesus sacrificed his all for sinful humanity. Empower us to love as you first loved us, O God, our strength.

Amen.

Thirty-second Sunday in Ordinary Time

Scripture:

1 Kings 17:10–16
Psalm 146:7, 8–9, 9–10
Hebrews 9:24–28
Mark 12:38–44
   [or (short form) 12:41–44]

Focus:

STEWARDSHIP

Reflection

Directions: Consider the First Reading and the Gospel for the Thirty-second Sunday in Ordinary Time. Then answer these questions:

1. *What do these readings tell you about God's generosity?*

2. *What example do these readings set for you?*

3. *When have you followed the example of the two widows?*

4. *What keeps you from following their example?*

Questions

1. *What criteria do you use to determine success?*

2. *Who in this Gospel would you describe as the true disciple of Jesus? Why?*

3. *What is the challenge of this Gospel for you?*

Quotable Quote:

The Second Vatican Council states: *"[Our love for Christ] is not something reserved for important matters, but must be exercised above all in the ordinary circumstances of daily life, . . . Christ is now at work in the hearts of [all] by the power of his Spirit; not only does he arouse in them a desire for the world to come but he quickens, purifies, and strengthens the generous aspirations of [humankind] to make life more humane and conquer the earth for this purpose."* (GS 38)

Memorable People:

Saint Catherine of Siena (d. 1380) described a revelation she had from God, whose voice urges us to generosity. She wrote that the divine directed her: "And so I have given many gifts and graces, both spiritual and temporal, with such diversity that I have not given everything to one single person, so that you may be constrained to practice charity toward one another. . . . I have willed that one should need another and that all should be my ministers in distributing the graces and gifts they have received from me."

The Church Says:

We have each been given a certain unique collection of gifts from above, and it is our duty and our joy to employ those gifts in a wise and loving manner to build up the kingdom of God.

Those who live as good Christian stewards find the proper meaning and orientation to their lives, their actions, and their decision of how to apportion the resources God has given them. The two basic stances in the practice of stewardship are: one celebrates God's creation and the other, God's Redemption. Christian stewards collaborate with God in the work of creation. We can appreciate and sustain the beauty of this world through ecological awareness and actions to cultivate a sense of interdependence and solidarity. Christian stewards also collaborate with God in the work of Redemption by asking for the grace of conversion, the grace to repent, change, and grow and to become good examples of self-giving and sacrifice. Christian stewards also bear a responsibility to build up the Church in every aspect.

For This Week:

I want to remember:

I want to put my faith into action by:

Questions to Explore

Prayer for the Week

God of this vast universe, you have created us in your image and likeness, empowering us to experience wonder and joy at the goodness of all of life. Each day the beauty of your wonderful world surrounds us.

Give us the eyes to see your marvelous works, the ears to hear the music of life, and the conviction to respond to the needs of others.

Give us generous and thankful hearts, that we might share all our blessings to build your kingdom here and now. We want to live in the blessed assurance that Christ will come again to embrace us.

Empower us in the living Spirit, breathed into us from creation's dawn.

Amen.

Thirty-third Sunday in Ordinary Time

Scripture:

Daniel 12:1–3
Psalm 16:5, 8, 9–10, 11
Hebrews 10:11–14, 18
Mark 13:24–32

Focus:

FINAL JUDGMENT

Reflection

Directions:

1. *Apocalyptic events, those occurrences telling about the end of the world, are described in movies, on television shows, on radio talk programs, and in magazines. On the scale below, with 10 at the high end, circle the number where you put yourself on this scale, regarding how much you think about the end times.*

1	2	3	4	5	6	7	8	9	10

Then list four feelings you have about the end times.

2. *As you think about how you will be judged, what changes in lifestyle do you desire?*

Quotable Quote:

The Book of Revelation (21:5–6) depicts Christ at the end of time: *"And the one who was seated on the throne said, 'See, I am making all things new. . . . I am the Alpha and the Omega, the beginning and the end. To the thirsty I will give water as a gift from the spring of the water of life.'"* Christ is called "the Alpha and Omega" at the lighting of the Easter Candle at the Easter Vigil.

Did You Know?

Christ has been depicted artistically as a judge. In these representations, Christ assumes the judge's posture, seated upon a throne, with a globe (representing the world) held in one hand. His other hand is held upright in blessing with his first two fingers extended (representing Jesus' full humanity and divinity, by which he saves us). Sometimes even the infant Jesus seated upon Mary's lap in a painting or statue is portrayed holding the globe.

The Church Says:

Christ came into the world as part of God's plan of Salvation. Through his life, Death, and Resurrection, Christ redeemed the world. God chose to put all of creation, including human life, under Christ. The Lord of all of life, Christ is also the judge in whose light the truth is revealed.

The Creed states that Christ will judge the living and the dead. The Church teaches that there are two judgments. The first, called particular judgment, is the judging of the moral quality of each one's life. This judgment occurs immediately after death, when Christ determines whether the person has fundamentally chosen to cooperate with God's grace or to reject it. The other, final judgment, refers to the end time in history when Christ will come again, bringing the fullness of God's kingdom, and sum up everything by passing definitive judgment on all people, nations, and creation itself. In light of the Gospel message, Christ judges each according to how he or she lived in accord with the kingdom imperative to love one's neighbor, thus expressing wholehearted love for God. At the Last Judgment, Christ, the living Word, will reveal God's glorious triumph over evil and at the same time manifest the ultimate meaning of the whole work of creation.

Scriptural descriptions of the end times with apocalyptic imagery are not to be understood literally. No one knows when the end of the world will be. Besides cataclysmic imagery, the Bible also contains wonderful images of Christ's triumph, of the Lamb seated on the throne, with thousands of people gathered from every nation, dressed in white (baptismal) robes, singing praise to God and to the Lamb.

For This Week:

I want to remember:

I want to put my faith into action by:

Questions to Explore

Prayer for the Week

Lord Jesus Christ,
we give you honor and praise,
and glory now and forever.
Teach our hearts your ways
that we may always live with you.
Make us faithful messengers of your kingdom,
that all our sisters and brothers
may come to know the riches you offer.
Call us, your elect, to your side.
Let your coming in glory at the end of time
be a time of rejoicing for each of us,
as we strive to live out
your command of love in this life.
Amen.

Thirty-fourth Sunday in Ordinary Time

Scripture:

Daniel 7:13–14
Psalm 93:1, 1–2, 5
Revelation 1:5–8
John 18:33–37

Focus:

CHRIST THE KING

Reflection

Directions: *Reflect upon the meaning of Christ the King by allowing these images to speak to your heart. Then write down your insights after each, using the formula, Christ's kingship is . . .*

A kingdom not of this world. Christ's kingship is . . .

I came into this world to testify to the truth. Christ's kingship is . . .

Anyone committed to the truth hears my voice. Christ's kingship is . . .

The faithful witness. Christ's kingship is . . .

The firstborn of the dead. Christ's kingship is . . .

Freed us from our sins by his own blood. Christ's kingship is . . .

The Alpha and Omega. Christ's kingship is . . .

Questions

1. *What metaphors or images would you use to describe the kingdom of God?*

2. *When and how have you experienced the invitation of Christ to surrender yourself to his kingdom?*

3. *How has the Church, in her people and her worship, made the kingdom a reality for you?*

Did You Know?

The blessing prayer for a new font petitions: "Grant, O Lord, that the people who are reborn from this font may fulfill in their actions what they pledge by their faith and show by their lives what they begin by the power of your grace. Let the people of different nations and conditions who come forth as one from these waters . . . show by their love . . . that they are citizens of the one kingdom."

The Church Says:

The theme of the kingdom of God permeates the life and teaching of Jesus. This kingdom indicates the very real dominion of God among us and also is a metaphor for eternity spent in the divine presence. Our Redemption won through the life, ministry, Death, and Resurrection of Jesus unites us all with one another and in union with Christ. Thus, all people are invited to enter the kingdom of God, particularly the poor and lowly.

Jesus asks for a radical choice from his followers, to give everything in order to obtain the treasure of the kingdom. In the life of the Church and the Sacraments we catch a glimpse of the fullness of God's reign. In the blessed hope of inheriting the kingdom we proclaim Christ as King and place our lives at the service of his dominion. Christ who reigns from the wood of the Cross is exalted and we who are moved by grace to surrender to his reign anticipate the glory yet to be revealed.

For This Week:

I want to remember:

I want to put my faith into action by:

Questions to Explore

Prayer for the Week

Christ our King, you are the Ancient One, promised from the beginning. Your earthly coming and Death on the Cross freed us from sin and made of us a royal nation in the service of God. Your kingdom is an everlasting reign, steadfast and glorious.

For you are the Alpha and Omega, the beginning and the end. At the end of time you will come on a throne of glory and power to judge the living and the dead.

May the power of your kingship over the cosmos deeply touch our hearts as we surrender our lives to your dominion.

Amen.

HOLY DAYS AND FEASTS

The Immaculate Conception of the Blessed Virgin Mary

Scripture:

Genesis 3:9–15, 20
Psalm 98:1, 2–3, 3–4
Ephesians 1:3–6, 11–12
Luke 1:26–38

Focus:

THE IMMACULATE CONCEPTION OF THE BLESSED VIRGIN MARY

Reflection

Directions: *In the space below are the opening lines from today's Gospel. Read these prayerfully, and then use your imagination to write your description of Mary, favored daughter of God and wholly integrated (sinless) woman. You may choose to write in the form of a poem, a symbolic story (like the story of Adam and Eve), or a short scene from a movie or play.*

"Greetings, favored one! The Lord is with you." "Do not be afraid, Mary, for you have found favor with God."

Questions

1. How has God's grace overcome sin in your personal experiences?

2. What can you learn from these stories of Eve and Mary?

3. What does this doctrine of the Immaculate Conception of Mary awaken in you?

Quotable Quote:

Pope Paul VI stipulates *Guidelines for Devotion to the Blessed Virgin Mary* (1974), saying, *"The ultimate purpose of devotion to the Blessed Virgin is to glorify God and lead Christians to commit themselves to a life which conforms absolutely to his will."*

Did You Know?

In 1846, the bishops of the United States chose Mary under the title of the Immaculate Conception to be the patroness of this relatively new country. Soon after that, the building of a shrine in her honor in Washington, D.C., was begun. This shrine, called the National Shrine of the Immaculate Conception, is located at the edge of the campus of the Catholic University of America.

The Church Says:

Today's Solemnity celebrates that from the moment of her conception in the womb of Anne, Mary was free from Original Sin and all its effects. This special grace from God flows out of Mary's role in God's plan for the Salvation of humankind. The doctrine of the Immaculate Conception is not found in Scripture. However, since the earliest days of the Church, the belief that Mary was free from the stain of Original Sin has been upheld. Pope Pius IX declared the doctrine of Mary's Immaculate Conception an infallible dogma on December 8, 1854. This favor bestowed upon Mary is not a result of something she did but is the action of God upon her. This is also true in our lives. Everything depends on gift—grace from God.

Mary's "yes" to the invitation to become the mother of God gives her an esteemed place in Salvation History and provides for us a model of a true disciple, that is, conformity to God's will. The breach with God described in the Genesis account of Adam and Eve disobeying God's command has been made whole through the obedient submission of Mary to God's plan for the Salvation of humanity.

For This Week:

I want to remember:

I want to put my faith into action by:

Questions to Explore

Prayer for the Week

Loving and gracious God,
we thank and praise you on this day
for the gift of Mary, your Mother.
You honored this simple woman
with the favor of sinlessness.
You gave Mary the privilege of conceiving
and bearing your beloved Son.
Her "yes" to the angel's announcement
opened the way for our Salvation.

O Mary, conceived without sin,
pray that we too might respond
in faithfulness and love to God,
and thus also bear Christ
in today's world. Amen.

Mary, the Holy Mother of God

Scripture:

Numbers 6:22–27
Psalm 67:2–3, 5, 6, 8
Galatians 4:4–7
Luke 2:16–21

Focus:

THEOTOKOS

Reflection

Directions: *From the Gospel and the teaching on Mary, Mother of God, write down three to five characteristics or qualities evident in Mary. When you have finished, choose the quality you believe God is inviting you to manifest in your own life. Write a short, concrete description of how you could incorporate that quality in your own life.*

Qualities of Mary:

In my life . . .

Questions

1. *What experience of Christ in your life do you treasure in your heart?*

2. *How does Mary, Mother of God, known as Theotokos, influence your life?*

Quotable Quote:

"Mary treasured all these words and pondered them in her heart."
(Luke 2:19)

Did You Know?

Federico Barocci (1575–1579) captures Mary, the Mother of God, in one of her aspects as universal mother. In his painting entitled "Madonna del Popolo" (Mother of the People), the Virgin intercedes for us. She is being blessed by Christ in the heavens, supported by cherubs under which is a dove, representing the Holy Spirit. The dove hovers over a crowd of adults and children, both rich and poor. A wealthy mother points to the apparition of Christ and Mary, but her young children are more interested in the byplay between a beggar and a street musician. The whole piece is full of movement and life, including Mary's loving gaze upon her Son and the motion of her hands as they present to him the people below.

The Church Says:

During this Christmas season, the Church celebrates this Solemnity of Mary because of her role in Christ's birth. The Church proclaimed that Mary is truly the Mother of God at the Council of Ephesus in 431. The Greek word used for this solemnity, theotokos, means one who has given birth to God. Jesus is truly human and divine, one person with two natures. The Church arrived at the truth that for Mary to be the Mother of Jesus means that she is the mother of God as well as the mother of Jesus in his humanity. Mary is inseparably linked with the saving work of her Son. The Church honors Mary because she freely cooperated in the work of our Salvation through her faith and obedience.

For This Week:

I want to remember:

I want to put my faith into action by:

Questions to Explore

Prayer for the Week

God, you are the source of light in the world.
You have sent your Son, Jesus,
*   to dwell among your people*
*   through the womb of Mary, your Mother.*
Marvelous are your works, O God!
Mary, through her faithful love,
*   gave birth to the Savior,*
*   called Wonderful God, Prince of Peace.*
We ask that Mary's fidelity,
*   born of a humble heart,*
*   encourage us to bear your light and peace*
*   in our world.*
We ask this through Christ,
*   your Word made flesh.*
Amen.

The Presentation of the Lord

Scripture:

Malachi 3:1–4
Psalm 24:7, 8, 9, 10
Hebrews 2:14–18
Luke 2:22–40 or 2:22–32

Focus:

THE TWO NATURES

Reflection

Directions: *As you listen to the Gospel from Luke 2:22–40, place yourself in the position of Simeon, Anna, and Jesus' parents. Then in the three columns below indicate what each of these characters in the account reveals to you about the nature of Jesus.*

SIMEON   ANNA   MARY and JOSEPH

Questions

1. *What about the nature of Jesus has been revealed to you through the people and the circumstances of your life?*

2. *In the light of the observations of these holy people and your own experience, who is Jesus?*

Did You Know?

In the northern hemisphere this feast is celebrated in the dead of winter darkness. The assembly gathers prior to the liturgy outside the church and candles are blessed. As these blessed candles are lit, the people process into church singing and the Mass of the Presentation of the Lord is celebrated. Customarily, enough candles are blessed on this day in order to last through the year. Thus, this feast also goes by the name "Candlemas."

The Church Says:

The Catholic Church confesses belief in Jesus, the Second Person of the Blessed Trinity, as possessing two natures. That is, Jesus Christ is fully human and fully divine. While this is based in the Apostles' experience of him and is asserted by Scripture, the theological understanding of this doctrine was first addressed by the Council of Chalcedon in 451 due to the Monophysite controversy (or heresy). The Monophysites charged that the human nature of Christ ceased to exist when the divine person of the Son of God assumed it.

The Council of Chalcedon proclaimed, "Following the holy Father, we unanimously teach and confess one and the same Son, our Lord Jesus Christ: the same perfect in divinity and perfect in humanity, the same truly God and truly man, composed of rational soul and body; consubstantial with the Father as to his divinity and consubstantial with us as to his humanity; 'like us in all things but sin.'" The Council then answered the Monophysites and asserted, "We confess that one and the same Christ . . . is to be acknowledged in two natures without confusion, change, division, or separation. The distinction between the natures was never abolished by their union, but rather the character proper to each of the two natures was preserved as they came together in one person . . ." (Council of Chalcedon, DS 301–2).

Another way the Church expresses this is to assert that Jesus is both the Son of God and the Son of the Virgin Mary. The two natures of Christ, one divine and one human, are not confused, but united. They are united in the one person of Jesus Christ. This union does not cease.

For This Week:

I want to remember:

I want to put my faith into action by:

 ## Questions to Explore

 ## Prayer for the Week

Jesus, we desire to be messengers of your Good News. There are many in this world who need to hear the message of your human and divine presence with us. In your humanity, you have walked with us, felt the pains and joys of living, and have loved much. In your divinity, you are our source of sustenance and transformation. We raise up to you not only ourselves, but those whose names be presented to this circle of prayer. You, who promised to be with us as we gather, have heard our cry. Give us the courage to share all that you have come to mean in our lives. Give us the words to speak the glory of your presence and promise—Son of God and Child of Mary. Prepare the hearts of those we bring before you that they might hear all that you have accomplished in your living, dying, and rising. Amen.

The Ascension of the Lord

Scripture:

Acts 1:1–11
Psalm 47:2–3, 6–7, 8–9
Ephesians 1:17–23
Mark 16:15–20

Focus:

THE ASCENSION OF THE LORD

Question:

1. *What do you feel as you picture Jesus ascending to Heaven?*

2. *What does the Ascension mean for you?*

Quotable Quotes:

Jesus Christ . . . has gone into heaven and is at the right hand of God, with angels, authorities, and powers made subject to him. (1 Peter 3:22)

He was lifted up, and a cloud took him out of their sight . . . Why do you stand looking up toward heaven? This Jesus, who has been taken up from you into heaven, will come in the same way as you saw him go into heaven. (Acts 1:9, 11)

Did You Know?

The Solemnity of the Ascension of the Lord was celebrated from the later years of the fourth century. The celebration in the early years included a procession to the Mount of Olives, where the Ascension is said to have occurred. The Ascension, one of the Glorious Mysteries, is an image used in praying the Rosary.

Regarding this solemnity, the Church instructs us: On the fortieth day after Easter or, where it is not a holy day of obligation, on the Seventh Sunday of Easter, the Ascension of the Lord is celebrated. This solemnity directs our attention to Christ, who ascended into heaven before the eyes of the disciples, who now is seated at the right hand of the Father, invested with royal power, who is there to prepare a place for us in the kingdom of heaven, and who is destined to come again at the end of time."

The Church Says:

Christ died. The Messiah suffered, died, and was buried for our Salvation. But Christ has risen. For the disciples the Resurrection vindicated Christ's life and revealed to them the fulfillment of God's promised kingdom. Christ will come again. Because of his Ascension, Christ was no longer bound to earthly existence. Christ comes now in a new way and with him is the dawning of a new age, the final age promised by God. This new age is characterized by the renewal of God's presence through the Spirit.

For This Week:

I want to remember:

I want to put my faith into action by:

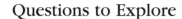

Questions to Explore	Prayer for the Week

	Lord Jesus,
	   you ascended in glory.
	You are my hope.
	May I follow you into the new creation.
	Until that time may I have the joy
	   of experiencing your presence with me
	   as you promised.
	Amen.

The Most Holy Trinity

Scripture:

Deuteronomy 4:32–34, 39–40
Psalm 33:4–5, 6, 9, 18–19, 20, 22
Romans 8:14–17
Matthew 28:16–20

Focus:

THE HOLY TRINITY

Reflection

Directions: *The Bible has many references of the Three Persons of the Blessed Trinity. Brainstorm places in the Bible that refer to each of the Three Persons of God and list them below. When you have finished, list the various qualities and names you associate with each Person of the Trinity.*

	FATHER	JESUS	HOLY SPIRIT
Scripture			
Qualities			
Names			

Reflect on your own experiences of the Three Persons of God.

Which Person of the Trinity do you think about and pray to the most often?

When do you pray to this Person, and when do you pray to the other Persons of the Trinity?

What changes have occurred over time in your relationship with the Persons of the Trinity?

Quotable Quotes:

The Eucharistic Prayer of the Mass concludes with a doxology, a prayer praising the Trinity: *"Through him [Christ], and with him, and in him, O God, almighty Father, in the unity of the Holy Spirit, all glory and honor is yours, for ever and ever." (RM, Eucharist Prayers)* While the Solemnity of the Most Holy Trinity specifically focuses on the triune God, the work of Salvation and the life of the Trinity is celebrated at every Mass.

Did You Know?

The Solemnity of the Most Holy Trinity is an "idea feast," commemorating an aspect of Catholic doctrine rather than an event in Salvation history. As early as the ninth century, Alcuin (d. 804), Abbot under Charlemagne, composed a votive Mass for the Trinity. In 1334, during the Avignon captivity, Pope John XXII approved the feast and extended it to the universal Church.

The Church Says:

The doctrine of the Trinity, Three Persons in One God, is at the heart of the Christian faith because it is the mystery of God's very self. Christian faith is founded on belief in the Trinity. The Church baptizes "in the name of the Father, and of the Son, and of the Holy Spirit."

The doctrine of the Trinity is found in the Apostles' Creed, and again in the Nicene Creed, formulated in 325. This creed expresses faith in a God of three equal persons who have no beginning or end. This belief arises out of and proclaims a continuing human experience of God as Father, Son, and Spirit. From the time of Jesus, the Spirit is further identified as the Spirit of Jesus, continuing the mission of Jesus to bring about the Reign of God in the world.

The Church expresses this threefold experience of God in the baptismal formula, in Scripture (for example, 2 Corinthians 13:13 and Ephesians 4:6), in preaching, catechesis, and the prayer of the Church. Mass and many other prayer sessions begin with the words used at Baptism: "In the name of the Father, and of the Son, and of the Holy Spirit." The Roman Missal, containing the Mass prayers, concludes prayers with: "Through our Lord Jesus Christ, your Son, who lives and reigns with you in the unity of the Holy Spirit, one God, for ever and ever."

Traditional Catholic theology uses the terms "substance," "essence," and "nature" to indicate the oneness of God. The term "person" distinguishes the Father, Son, and Spirit. The word "relation" indicates that their distinction lies in the relationship each person has to the others.

For This Week:

I want to remember:

I want to put my faith into action by:

Questions to Explore

Prayer for the Week

In the name of the Father, and of the Son,
and of the Holy Spirit. Amen.

God, you are compassionate,
rich in kindness and slow to anger.
I praise you, who are Creator, Savior,
and Spirit of peace and love.
Teach my heart to recognize you
in your creative energy,
in your dying and rising,
and in your powerful and gentle movements.
May I know your love in the love I experience
and share with my sisters and brothers.
Glory to you, Father, Son, and Spirit.
Amen.

The Most Holy Body and Blood of Christ

Scripture:

Exodus 24:3–8
Psalm 116
Hebrews 9:11–15
Mark 14:12–16, 22–26

Focus:

THE REAL PRESENCE OF JESUS IN THE EUCHARIST

Reflection

Directions: *Below are several images taken from the Scriptures for this solemnity. Allow the full import of these images to enter your heart as you read through the list. After this reflection, compose a poem or prayer that describes the meaning of the Body and Blood of Christ for you. Express your longing for participating in the Eucharist if you are a catechumen or candidate. If a sponsor or team member, express your joy in participating in the Sacrament and sacrifice of the Eucharist.*

Blood splashed on the altar, sprinkled on the people

The blood of the covenant which the Lord has made with you

The cup of salvation

A sacrifice of thanksgiving

The blood of Christ offered up unblemished to God

Christ the mediator of the new covenant

Sacrifice the paschal lamb

Bread taken, blessed, and broken, and given to them

"This is my Body." (Mark 14:22)

Took a cup, gave thanks and passed it to them, and they all drank from it

"This is my blood, of the covenant, which is poured out for many." (Mark 14:24)

Drink of the fruit of the vine in the reign of God

Did You Know?

"This feast, which traditionally involves a solemn procession with the eucharistic bread, developed in the 13th century. . . . Corpus Christi retains its theological significance as a celebration of God's gift of Christ in the Spirit to the church and world as its food and drink of everlasting life. Moreover, in the celebration of this feast the church as the body of Christ experiences itself called to let the Spirit fashion it more and more into bread and drink for the world."

"In its devotion the Church has handed down as a distinctive feature of the celebration of this solemnity a procession in which the eucharist is carried solemnly and with singing through the streets, and the Christian people give public witness to their belief in the sacrament of the eucharist and to their devotion" (CB 386). Corpus Christi processions are colorful affairs, sometimes mobilizing entire groups within a parish to participate. Musicians play hymns, children serve, carrying candles, while adults carry banners and sometimes a silk canopy under which the Blessed Sacrament is carried by a priest or deacon. The host is held in a special container called a monstrance (from the Latin for "showing") made for just this purpose. The monstrance can be simple or quite ornate. It is fashioned so that the host sits in a glass holder so that all can see as it is held aloft.

The Church Says:

In remembrance of Jesus' action at the Last Supper, in the Eucharist we recall the sacrifice of the Lord and offer again to God the gifts of bread and wine through the power of the Holy Spirit and the words of Christ. The Sacrament of Eucharist is the source and summit of Christian life. The bread and wine are changed into the Body and Blood of Christ. When we eat this bread and drink this cup, although we taste the fruits of Earth and our human hands, it is the Body and Blood of our Lord and Savior who sacrificed himself on our behalf who nourishes us.

From the earliest time, the Church taught and continues to teach that Christ is really present under the appearances of the bread and wine, that is, real in the fullest sense, a substantial presence by which Christ, both divine and human, makes himself wholly and entirely present. A substantial change takes place within the elements of bread and wine. Traditionally the Church has called this "transubstantiation." This Eucharistic presence of Christ continues as long as the Eucharistic species (the bread and wine) exist. We also believe that the Real Presence of Jesus is present wholly and totally in each of the elements, such that while an individual in connection with the celebration of the Eucharist consumes only the Eucharistic bread, the whole Christ is received, and if only the Eucharistic wine is consumed, the whole Christ is received. The Church also teaches that at Mass Christ is recognized and present in the assembly of people who gather, in the person of the presider, in the proclamation of the Word, and most especially in the Eucharistic species (CCC 1088).

For This Week:

I want to remember:

I want to put my faith into action by:

Questions to Explore

Prayer for the Week

God of love, you chose us to be your people. We are precious in your eyes and you have gathered us to yourself.

In the presence of your Church, we pledge our faithfulness to live out your Laws and follow the way of Jesus.

In his sacrifice of blood he raised us to your eternal inheritance. We, your sons and daughters, now share the cup of blessing in our Covenant of love with you.

Amen.

The Nativity of Saint John the Baptist

Scripture:

Isaiah 49:1–6
Psalm 139:1–3, 13–14, 14–15
Acts 13:22–26
Luke 1:57–66, 80

Focus:

HUMAN COOPERATION WITH DIVINE GRACE

Questions:

1. *What are some of your feelings about God's action or important stories around the birth of a child in your family?*

2. *What begins to happen in people as a result of Zechariah's being struck mute and then finding his speech at the time of the naming of John?*

3. *What newness is God initiating in you? Be more specific in your example than being part of this process to become Catholic.*

4. *Make a time line of John the Baptist's life and put on it all the things you know about John the Baptist.*

5. *What kinds of words, e.g., strong, fearsome, comforting, usually move you to change?*

6. *Who are messengers you know who remind you that God's kingdom is now?*

Quotable Quotes:

*Among those born of women no one is greater than John;
yet the least in the kingdom of God is greater than he.* Luke 7:28

*The Lord called me before I was born,
while I was in my mother's womb he named me.* Isaiah 49:1

Did You Know?

The Church's liturgical calendar only celebrates three births: that of Jesus, Mary, and John the Baptist. All other Saints' feasts are celebrated on the day of their death, the date of their birth into eternal life. John the Baptist was an important herald and witness to Christ, the true Light of the world.

The Church Says:

John the Baptist is an important and pivotal figure in the Gospel. He was the last Jewish prophet and made the Savior known when he came. Stories surrounding John's birth, from the announcement by the angel and the striking mute of his father, Zechariah, to his leaping in Elizabeth's womb upon Mary's visitation to Elizabeth, are wonderful and are found in Luke's Gospel. The clear and amazing action of God in his coming alerts the community that something new has begun. Some scholars believe John may have lived an ascetic life with the Essene community at Qumran. When he began his public ministry, he wore camel's hair cloth and ate locusts and wild honey. Coming out of the wilderness John preached a strong message of repentance to prepare the way for the Savior's coming. Because he told Herod's brother it was unlawful to have a certain wife, Herod had him imprisoned and eventually had him beheaded to fulfill a request from Herodias's daughter. In his preaching John continually prepared the way for Christ.

For This Week:

I want to remember:

I want to put my faith into action by:

Questions to Explore

Prayer for the Week

Thank you, God,
for the gift of John the Baptist.
When I hear your message
to repent and change,
may I listen and respond.
Use me as your messenger
to prepare the way for your fuller coming
in our world today.
Make my voice strong.
Guide me in your truth.
I pray through Christ,
the Light of the world.
Amen.

Saints Peter and Paul, Apostles

Scripture:

Acts 12:1–11
Psalm 34:2–3, 4–5, 6–7, 8–9
2 Timothy 4:6–8, 17–18
Matthew 16:13–19

Focus:

COLLEGIALITY

Questions:

1. *What do you think it was like for Peter to be called "rock" by Christ, to have the keys entrusted to him, and to live this out in his life?*

2. *What is an image of faith for you?*

3. *Name all the Popes you are able to and anything you know about them.*

4. *State anything you know about the Second Vatican Council, e.g., when and where it was held, who attended, and any documents or results of the Council.*

5. *What are you aware of as being the work of the bishops' conference in this country?*

Did You Know?

Paul, who first persecuted the Church, had his name changed by God from Saul at the time of his conversion. He is considered the preeminent missionary of the Gospel to the Gentile world.

Rocks have long denoted holy or special places. The various stones in the British Isles, e.g., Stonehenge, circles of stones in Avebury, stones in the form of a large Celtic cross in Callenish, Scotland, and stones at Newgrange in Ireland, mark sacred sites.

According to an ancient custom of the Church, an ordaining bishop who is consecrating a new bishop must, ordinarily, be assisted by two other bishops who co-consecrate. The three of them together signify the whole body of bishops.

An ecumenical council is the most concrete example of collegiality. The whole body of bishops acts in union with the Pope in their deliberations and decisions. Another form of leadership within the Church that manifests collegial workings are specific groupings of bishops organized around provinces, patriarchies, regions, or bishops' conferences by countries. In less concrete fashion, collegiality is also manifested by individual bishops throughout the world who show their concern for the universal Church by governing well their own local diocese.

The Church Says:

The faith was spread to both Jews and Gentiles through the activity of Peter and Paul. Jesus handed over to Peter authority for the founding of a church. This is symbolized when Jesus gives to Peter the keys of the Kingdom of Heaven. Jesus gives the power to bind and to loose, which is viewed as the teaching authority. Jesus calls Peter the "rock," the first leader following Jesus. Peter has come to be called the first Pope, and all Popes are successors of Peter. The office is sometimes referred to as "the chair of Peter."

The Pope is also the bishop of Rome, which is understood as the foundation of unity in the Church. Collegiality is a Catholic teaching that describes an essential element in the ecclesial ministry of the bishop. This element derives from Jesus, who at the start of his own public ministry called the Twelve to follow him. Selected by Christ and formed as a group, the disciples were sent on mission together. Thus, Catholic bishops today, who are the successor Apostles, exercise their episcopal ministry from within a similar group created by Christ, that is, the college of bishops. They cannot exercise this ministry, however, without also being in communion with the bishop of Rome, the successor of Saint Peter and head of this college of bishops. In our own times, the Second Vatican Council also addressed the reality of how the college of bishops functions. The Council reiterated that the body of bishops is the successor to the college of Apostles and affirmed that, "Together, with their head, the pope, and never apart from him, they have supreme and full authority over the universal Church; but this power cannot be exercised without the agreement of the Roman Pontiff" (LG 22).

For This Week:

I want to remember:

I want to put my faith into action by:

Questions to Explore

Prayer for the Week

I thank you, God, for Peter and Paul
*   and their untiring and unwavering faith.*
You have built the Church
*   upon the rock of Peter's faith.*
Bless the Church with a solid faith.
May Paul's example inspire me
*   and the entire Church to proclaim her faith.*
May Peter and Paul's untiring witness
*   and prayers lead me to full life with Christ.*
I pray through Christ,
*   who is Lord now and for ever.*
Amen.

The Transfiguration of the Lord

Scripture:

Daniel 7:9–10, 13–14
Psalm 97:1–2, 5–6, 9
2 Peter 1:16–19
Mark 9:2–10

Focus:

VISIONS AND PRIVATE REVELATIONS

Reflection

Meditation: *Reflect on the experience of Hildegard of Bingen. She received visions that were interpreted with the help of a voice from Heaven. Here is a description of one vision: "It happened that, in the eleven hundred and forty-first year of the Incarnation of the Son of God, Jesus Christ, when I was forty-two years and seven months old, heaven was opened and a fiery light of exceeding brilliance came and permeated my whole breast, not like a burning but like a warming flame, as the sun warms anything its rays touch. And immediately I knew the meaning of the exposition of the Scriptures. . . . I had sensed in myself wonderfully the power and mystery of secret and admirable visions from childhood—that is, from the age of five—up to that time, as I do now. This, however, I showed to no one except a few religious persons who were living in the same manner as I" [Hildegard of Bingen, Scivias, trans. by Mother Columba Hart and Jane Bishop (Mahwah, NJ: Paulist Press, 1990), pp. 59–60)].*

1. *Begin to write your experience and the feelings gleaned from this meditation.*

2. *Describe a time when you had a similar experience of awe and wonder at God's glorified presence.*

Did You Know?

The Catholic Church has been graced with notable mystics throughout its history. Some of them have left behind writings that detailed, as best they could, their mystical experiences, visions, and private revelations. While the record of these experiences are not part of the binding teaching of the Church, in many instances it is regarded as a kind of literature of the Spirit. Examples of mystics who have recorded their experiences are:

Saint Bernard of Clairvaux (d. 1153)

Saint Catherine of Siena (d. 1380)

Meister Eckhart (d. 1327)

Saint Hildegard of Bingen (d. 1179)

Saint John of the Cross (d. 1591)

Julian of Norwich (d. 1413)

Saint Teresa of Jesus (Teresa of Ávila) (d. 1582)

The Church Says:

God is fully revealed to us in the life, ministry, teaching, Death, and Resurrection of Jesus. We can come to understand God through Scripture and the tradition of the Church, the primary means of Revelation. In other words, everything that God chooses to communicate to us for our Salvation has been done in Jesus and no new "public" Revelation will be given before Christ comes a second time in glory. However, the content of Revelation, given in the person of Jesus, can be understood anew or freshly interpreted in the context of the world. Throughout the history of the Church, Christian mystics have claimed private experiences that reveal the activity of God.

Visions, or private revelations, approved by the Church as credible, are nonetheless not held by the Church to be part of the doctrine, or official teaching, of the faith. The approval is stated in the negative, that there is nothing in those visions or private revelations that would harm the faith. As for recent apparitions, the Church has not yet completed its investigation which it conducts very carefully.

For This Week:

I want to remember:

I want to put my faith into action by:

Questions to Explore

Prayer for the Week

*Jesus, you call us to follow you up
   the high mountain to behold your glory.
We are dazzled by your transfigured presence
   shining forth
   in the face of a newborn baby,
   the magnificence of the sunrise and sunset,
   the sheer power of the wind.
Your Revelation of the face of God
   in all of creation,
   in our times of deep prayer,
   in the intimacy of friends and lovers,
   reassures us that you will come again in glory.
You come again, day after day,
   until that time when we will
   behold you face to face.
Amen.*

The Assumption of the Blessed Virgin Mary

Scripture:

Revelation 11:19; 12:1–6, 10
Psalm 45:10–12, 16
1 Corinthians 15:20–26
Luke 1:39–56

Focus:

THE ASSUMPTION OF MARY

Reflection

1. *What does Mary's visit to Elizabeth and the Magnificat say about what kind of woman Mary was?*

2. *Name an image of Mary you want to carry with you.*

3. *What is your understanding of who Mary is for the Church?*

4. *How do you view prayer to Mary?*

5. *How is this feast of Mary's assumption a sign of hope to the Church?*

Quotable Quotes:

" *A great portent appeared in heaven: a woman clothed with the sun, with the moon under her feet, and on her head a crown of twelve stars. (Revelation 12:1)*

Blessed are you among women, and blessed is the fruit of your womb. (Luke 1:42)

My soul magnifies the Lord, and my spirit rejoices in God my Savior. (Luke 1:46) "

Did You Know?

On November 1, 1950, Pope Pius XII made the Assumption of Mary an official dogma of the Church in *Munificentissimus Deus.*

Mary is thought to have lived her last days with John the disciple in Ephesus.

Mary's death or her dormition, falling asleep, is portrayed on icons.

Zermatt, Switzerland, tucked in the shadow of the Matterhorn, annually holds a gigantic festival parade on the Solemnity of the Assumption.

The Church Says:

Mary, who was always a virgin and the mother of God, was assumed body and soul into Heaven at the time of her death. This is an honor God bestowed upon Mary, the mother of Christ. This honor ranks Mary as higher than all the Saints. As another human and as given to us as a mother at the foot of the Cross, Mary's assumption is a sign of hope for the pilgrim Church on Earth. One day the Church living and dead will be united at God's throne in Heaven.

For This Week:

I want to remember:

I want to put my faith into action by:

Questions to Explore

Prayer for the Week

God of life and death, I praise you.
Everything that has life comes from you.
I praise you for Mary,
*   who bore Christ in her womb,*
*   and whom you have raised body and soul*
*   to be with him in Heaven.*
May I follow her example
*   by responding wholeheartedly to you*
*   in all I say and do,*
*   and join with her someday*
*   in endless life and praise.*
I ask this through the Risen Christ. Amen.

The Exaltation of the Holy Cross

Scripture:

Numbers 21:4–9
Psalm 78:1–2, 34–35, 36–37, 38
Philippians 2:6–11
John 3:13–17

Focus:

REDEMPTION

Reflection

1. *How have you been lifted up and found life through the Cross?*

2. *Given the context of Jesus being lifted up as the serpent in the desert, what does it mean to believe in Jesus?*

3. *What cross are you embracing now in your life that you believe will lead to fuller life in Christ?*

4. *What are some of the ways Christ is Savior?*

5. *What other titles, besides Savior, does the Church give to Jesus?*

Quotable Quotes:

He [Jesus] humbled himself and became obedient to the point of death, even death on a cross. Therefore God also highly exalted him. (Philippians 2:8-9)

. . . the cross, though it has at its heart a collision and contradiction, can extend its four arms forever without altering its shape. Because it has a paradox at its centre it can grow without changing. The circle returns upon itself and is bound. The cross opens its arms to the four winds; it is a signpost for free travelers. (G. K. Chesterton)

Did You Know?

Various forms of the cross are in use in the Church. There is the form we are used to seeing upon which Jesus was hung, St. Brigid's cross with both sections being of equal length, the Tau Franciscan cross shaped like the Greek letter tau, the Celtic cross with a circle that cuts across the four sections of the cross, and the Jerusalem cross, which in addition to the four cross sections has smaller crosses in each of the four quadrants.

Many churches and baptismal fonts are constructed in the shape of a cross.

The expression "tree of life" comes from contrasting the cross to the tree in the Garden of Eden. The tree in Eden, the means of the first human sin through which death came into the world, is the tree of death. The Cross is the tree of life.

The Church Says:

The cross has become for Christians a sign of hope and of victory. Through Death on the Cross, Jesus was raised to new life. The mystery is that through embracing the Cross with Christ we are brought to new life. That is at the heart of the Christian faith. Sin and evil symbolized in death do not have ultimate power. God's love is more powerful. God reigns over everything. Christianity involves facing and embracing the cross that presents itself in various forms in life. Through his Death on the Cross, Jesus atones for our sins, or reconciles all things to himself. Christ is the Savior who saves through liberating, bringing Good News, giving sight, freeing the oppressed, forgiving, and healing. Christ lifts us up and is our sign of healing.

For This Week:

I want to remember:

I want to put my faith into action by:

Questions to Explore	Prayer for the Week

	Loving and gracious God,
	   through Christ you teach me
	   that the Cross is not only a means of suffering,
	   but also a Cross of triumph.
	I place the crosses I bear in your hands.
	Through bearing my cross with Christ,
	   may I one day share
	   in his glorious Resurrection.
	I pray through Christ, my Savior.
	Amen.

All Saints

Scripture:

Revelation 7:2–4, 9–14
Psalm 24:1–2, 3–4, 5–6
1 John 3:1–3
Matthew 5:1–12

Focus:

THE COMMUNION OF SAINTS

Reflection

Directions: *Think of people in your life who have had a positive influence on your life. They may be people you have known personally or people you have never met. In what way(s) have they influenced your life? What quality or qualities of their lives do you admire? Why? Write about these relationships which have influenced you to grow and change in the space below.*

Questions

1. *Describe how our society measures success.*

a traves de nuestros exitos personales

2. *Describe how God measures success.*

si nos dejamos trasformar por su Palabra y obras

3. *If you choose to follow in the footsteps of Christ, what will be the criteria by which you will be judged?*

Por mis obras, buenas y malas
Por el amor a Dios y al Projimo,

Did You Know?

The remote origins of this solemnity are found in the honor that early Christians paid to the martyrs, remembering them on the anniversary of their death, often at the very place of their martyrdom. After the age of persecution had ended, other holy individuals were gradually added to the list of those commemorated annually. In the fourth century, Saints were named in the Eucharistic Prayer. By the fifth century, a feast of All Saints was celebrated in certain churches of the Christian East. When Pope Bonfire transformed the Roman pantheon into a Christian church on May 13, 610, he designated that day as a feast of all Saints. It was under Gregory IV that the feast was moved to November 1, and thenceforth the observance spread throughout the West.

The Church Says:

All Christians are called to a life of holiness, that is, to conform ourselves to the image of Christ.

Saints (the word is derived from the Latin word for holy) are considered to be intercessors before God. They are not worshiped but venerated for the model of holiness that they offer to those of us still on Earth.

The Virgin Mary is venerated, with all the Saints, for her witness of holiness and her constant *fiat*, that is, her "yes" to God's will in seemingly impossible circumstances.

The Communion of Saints celebrates the one Body of the Church, with Christ as its Head. Those who have gone before us, those still on Earth, and those yet to come all share in the holiness of Christ as a holy people, sealed in the Blood of the Lamb.

For This Week:

I want to remember:

mi Padre y todas las Personas que an tenido Influencia en mi guia espiritual.

I want to put my faith into action by:

conocer la Palabra de Dios

Questions to Explore

Prayer for the Week

Holy God,
  we praise you for setting before us
  the witness of so many
  who have gone before us in faith:
All the martyrs, virgins, widows,
  teachers, holy men and women
  known for their actions on behalf of your
    kingdom.
We join with them as they cry out,
  "Salvation belongs to our God
  who is seated on the throne,
  and to the Lamb!" (Revelation 7:9)
"Amen! Blessing and glory and wisdom
  and thanksgiving and honor and power and
  might be to our God forever and ever! Amen."
(Revelation 7:12)

All Souls

Scripture:

Readings for All Souls may be taken from any of the Masses for the Dead See the Lectionary n. 789–93.

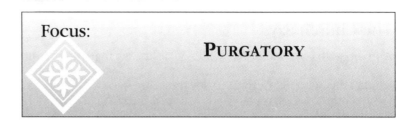

Focus:

PURGATORY

Reflection

Directions: *In the space below, write your own obituary, as you would like it to read at your death. Use the following as reference questions: When were you born? When did you die? What was the cause of your death? Who survived you? What will you be most remembered for? What was your biggest regret?*

Quotable Quotes:

Life is not lost by dying; life is lost minute by minute, day by day, in all the small uncaring ways. (Steven Vincent Benet)

Did You Know?

In Dante's *Divine Comedy*, Purgatory is a mountain rising from the ocean and divided into terraces, at the top of which is terrestrial paradise. Thomas Merton used Dante's image of a seven-tiered mountain as the symbol of the modern world in his autobiography, *The Seven Story Mountain*.

The Church Says:

In our Catholic understanding, Purgatory is a state of purification between death and Heaven whereby the remaining obstacles to the full enjoyment of one's personal and eternal union with God are removed. The obstacles which are removed are venial sins not repented at the time of death and any remaining effects or consequences to one's person of repented and forgiven mortal or deadly sins committed during one's earthly life. In our Catholic understanding, Purgatory is not an opportunity to reverse the course of one's earthly life. Conversion is not possible in Purgatory if conversion did not take place in life before death. Since an individual judgment follows immediately upon death, Purgatory is that interval after death that erases conditions preventing persons from enjoying full fellowship with God.

It is important to note that while Scripture refers to a cleansing fire (1 Corinthians 3:15; 1 Peter 1:7) and burning flames figure in some artistic depictions of Purgatory, the operative notion in Catholic doctrine and theology on Purgatory is that it is a state of purification, not punishment (CCC 1031). This state may even last only an instant, as we count time. What the doctrine upholds is that Purgatory is a transitional state which makes one ready for the experience of seeing God face-to-face in Heaven.

It is also important to note that the doctrine of Purgatory upholds an unbroken liturgical practice in our Church to making intercessory prayers for the dead. The Second Vatican Council observes, "In full consciousness of this communion of the whole Mystical Body of Jesus Christ, the Church in its pilgrim members, from the very earliest days of the Christian religion, has honored with great respect the memory of the dead; and, 'because it is a holy and a wholesome thought to pray for the dead that they may be loosed from their sins' (2 Maccabees 12:46) she offers her suffrages for them" (LG 50).

For This Week:

I want to remember:

I want to put my faith into action by:

Questions to Explore

Prayer for the Week

Prayer for the Souls in Purgatory:

*Eternal rest grant unto them, O Lord,
and may perpetual light shine upon them.
Amen.*

The Dedication of the Lateran Basilica

Scripture:

Isaiah 52:7–10
Psalm 98:1, 2–3, 3–4, 5–6
Hebrews 1:1–6
John 1:1–18 [or (short form) 1:1–5, 9–14]

Focus:

THE FOUR MARKS OF THE CHURCH

Reflection

Directions: *Reflect on and write your responses to the following questions: How do you feel about becoming a member of a universal Church? What hesitations, concerns, or questions do you have?*

Questions

1. What gift does being a part of a universal Church offer to you?

2. How are you called as an individual and as a community to work for unity among churches?

3. How do you hear yourself being called to holiness?

Did You Know?

The Lateran basilica is filled with venerable relics. The high altar itself is constructed over a wooden table which, as legend has it, St. Peter celebrated the Eucharist with the ancient Christians of Rome.
(Mary Ellen Hynes, *Companion to the Calendar*, LTP, Archdiocese of Chicago, 1993, p. 166)

The famous Lateran Treaty or "Concordat" agreed upon between the Vatican and Mussolini was finalized and signed at the Lateran Palace. The agreement stipulates that the Lateran grounds are also considered part of Vatican City State.

The Church Says:

The feast we celebrate today observes the anniversary of the dedication of the cathedral church of Rome. When the Emperor Constantine officially recognized Christianity, he made generous gifts to the Church, one of which was a palace and grounds formerly belonging to the Laterani family. In 324 he added a large church on the grounds named the Basilica of the Savior. Legend has it that the basilica was dedicated on November 9 that year. Later a baptistry was added and dedicated to St. John the Baptist. In subsequent years the entire edifice became known as St. John of the Lateran. Because it is the cathedral church of the bishop of Rome, the feast, at first observed only in Rome, was later extended to the whole Church as a sign of devotion to and of unity with the Chair of Peter. Thus, while this feast originates in a particular edifice in a particular place, it truly celebrates the universal Church which is apostolic, catholic, holy, and one.

For This Week:

I want to remember:

I want to put my faith into action by:

Questions to Explore

Prayer for the Week
Nicene Creed

I believe in one God,
the Father almighty,
maker of heaven and earth,
of all things visible and invisible.

I believe in one Lord Jesus Christ,
the Only Begotten Son of God,
born of the Father before all ages.
God from God, Light from Light,
true God from true God,
begotten, not made, consubstantial with
the Father;
through him all things were made.
For us men and for our salvation
he came down from heaven,
and by the Holy Spirit was incarnate
of the Virgin Mary,
and became man.

For our sake he was crucified under
Pontius Pilate,
he suffered death and was buried,

and rose again on the third day
in accordance with the Scriptures.
He ascended into heaven
and is seated at the right hand of the Father.

He will come again in glory
to judge the living and the dead
and his kingdom will have no end.

I believe in the Holy Spirit, the Lord,
the giver of life,
who proceeds from the Father and the Son,
who with the Father and the Son is
adored and glorified,
who has spoken through the prophets.

I believe in one, holy, catholic and
apostolic Church.
I confess one Baptism for the forgiveness
of sins and I look forward to the
resurrection of the dead and the life
of the world to come. Amen.

Glossary of Terms

Note: Those terms which display an asterisk* are themselves described elsewhere in the glossary.

Almsgiving

is the religious practice of giving from one's financial resources in order to assist or help those who are poorer and in need. This is commended by Jesus (Luke 18:22). St. Paul exhorts members of the Christian community at Corinth to give alms that they might be enriched by their very generous giving (2 Corinthians 9:11). On Ash Wednesday we Catholics hear from Matthew's Gospel—where Jesus teaches us to fast, pray, and give alms (Matthew 6:1-6, 16-18). Almsgiving is considered one of the three central penitential activities of Lent and a Work of Mercy. (The seven Corporal Works of Mercy are: to feed the hungry, to give drink to the thirsty, to clothe the naked, to visit prisoners, to give shelter to the homeless, to visit the sick, and to bury the dead). The word "alms" derives from the Greek, *eleos*, or "pity."

Anointing

is the coating, covering, or touching of a person or object with oil to convey a religious significance. The Old Testament refers to Moses' action in anointing the meeting tent, the Ark of the Covenant, and related religious objects with a special mixture of oil indicating the sacred status of these objects. Aaron and his sons were also anointed as priests (Exodus 30:27-30). Prophets and kings of Israel were anointed. The word "Christ" comes from the term "anointed" and is the title bestowed upon Jesus in the New Testament letters of Paul, indicating his role as priestly, prophetic, and kingly Messiah, the Lord's Anointed One who saves us (Isaiah 61:1). In contemporary liturgical usage, the Oil of Catechumens is used to anoint prior to Baptism and has its roots in ancient times when athletes were anointed before wrestling competitions. Sacred Chrism, a mixture of oil and perfume consecrated by the bishop, is used to anoint after Baptism, at Confirmation and at the ordination of priests and bishops. The Oil of the Sick is used to anoint sick persons and is specifically referenced in the New Testament (James 5). Chrism is also used to anoint altars and churches when they are dedicated.

Blessing

is the ritual expression of God's goodness and love. The action has traditionally communicated either the blessings of divine gifts bestowed upon us or our thankfulness for those gifts. Blessings are liturgical signs which call down God's holiness upon people or things. *The Book of Blessings* is a ritual book of the Church which lists several hundred prayer texts that express various types of blessings for individuals, groups, and objects. Types range from blessings of pregnant mothers, to catechists, to stained glass windows. The act of blessing is usually accomplished through certain prayers spoken and raising hands in benediction over the person or object, including making the Sign of the Cross.

Candidate

in the Catechumenate refers to a person who is baptized in another faith and who will be completing Christian initiation by being formally received into the Catholic Church. This term is also used in referring to a baptized Catholic who is seeking to complete Christian initiation through the celebration of Confirmation and Eucharist. Anyone seeking a Sacrament may be referred to as a candidate.

Canonization

is the process undertaken by the Church which leads to the declaration of sainthood. In the early Church the martyrs (those who died for the faith) were honored on the anniversary of their death and confessors (those who suffered for the faith) were also venerated. Later, exemplary Christians who led heroic lives of holiness were also acclaimed as Saints. Beginning in the thirteenth century, the process became more formal. In 1983, Pope John Paul II issued an apostolic constitution, *Divinus Perfectionis Magister* (Divine Teacher and Model of Perfection), which simplified the canonization process. Initially, a local bishop oversees the investigation into the life of the person in question, after which a biography, published writings, and information regarding possible miracles are submitted to the Vatican. The first step on the road to canonization is beatification (honoring the person with the title of "blessed"). If all requirements are met, then the person is canonized (given the title of "Saint," which derives from the Latin for "holy") by a declaration of the Pope at a solemn liturgy*.

Catechism

(from Greek, *katechein*, "to echo," or "to resound down"), is a manual of religious instruction usually presented in a simple and clear format. One of the first Catholic manuals was published after the Council of Trent in 1566 and intended to assist the clergy. An early catechism used in the United States was the *Baltimore Catechism*, commissioned by the bishops in 1885. In 1992 the Vatican issued the *Catechism of the Catholic Church*, a compendium of teachings which relies on Scripture, Tradition, and the teaching office (Magisterium) of the Church.

Catechumen

refers to a person who has attained the age of reason who is not baptized and who seeks Christian initiation (Baptism, Confirmation and Eucharist). One becomes a catechumen when the Church celebrates the Rite of Acceptance into the Order of Catechumens. This rite* is normally celebrated after the completion of a period of Inquiry or Pre-catechumenate, the first stage of the initiation process.

Contemplation

describes a particular prayer form which relies less on thinking and systematic thought processes and more on the direct experience of God's presence. While systematic meditation* may lead to contemplative prayer, this form is generally considered a gift from God and not the result of what one is doing in praying. Contemplation is described by many spiritual writers as the deepest type of prayer that involves the core of a person's being.

Conversion

characterizes the changes that occur in a person who embraces Jesus Christ. Those changes can be simultaneously evidenced in thought, word, and deed. Conversion takes place gradually over a period of time.

Creed

from Latin, *credo*, "I believe," is a pithy, official formulation of the tenets of the faith. The Apostles' Creed and the Nicene Creed are the two best-known examples of Christian creeds (either is mandated for use at Sunday Mass when the Church confesses its faith liturgically). In the course of Christian history, there have come down to us other creeds, such as the Athanasian Creed and the Creed of Hippolytus.

Discernment

describes the attempt to sift through an individual's or a group's experience to determine the call of the divine and where the Holy Spirit may be leading. It has also been called "Christian decision-making." It should be understood that discernment is ongoing in the life of the follower of Jesus and relies on private and liturgical prayer, the use of Scripture, and sometimes also the assistance of a Spiritual Director.

Doctrine

from Latin, *doctrina*, or "teaching," is an official statement by the Church of some aspect of teaching. Doctrine taught infallibly is also called a dogma*. In the Roman Catholic Church doctrine is formulated by the bishops acting together in concert with the Pope, such as at a synod or an ecumenical council. Core teachings or doctrines are also contained in Scripture and thus the Word of God "measures" all subsequent doctrinal statements.

Dogma

from Greek for "what seems right," this term describes a definitive teaching of the Church given infallibly (without error). The ability to declare a doctrine* infallible rests with the Pope, who does so in two areas: faith and morals.

Elect/Election

is the term applied to those catechumens who have been called by the Church to the celebration of the initiation Sacraments (Baptism, Confirmation and Eucharist) at Easter. The local bishop gives voice to this call at the celebration of the Rite of Election. In this sense, election does not describe the result of a political process or voting, but the action of God through the agency of the Church. In Sacred Scripture the elect are those freely chosen by God to receive the gift of Salvation and to bear witness to God.

Exorcism

is the Church's prayer which seeks to free persons from the power of evil. The New Testament reports that Jesus and his disciples engaged in such liberating actions. In the history of the Church two forms of exorcism have evolved. Major (or solemn) exorcisms seek to free a person from a persistent spiritual condition. Today these forms of exorcism are restricted to bishops or those priests whom they specially delegate. The other type of exorcism is found in the process of Christian initiation and consists of prayers and gestures expressing the Church's desire that those to be baptized be delivered from temptation and the power of evil. These "Minor Exorcisms" may be celebrated during the stage of the catechumenate. The "Scrutinies," which contain exorcism prayers, are celebrated on the Third, Fourth and Fifth Sundays of Lent with the elect*. The ritual used for the Baptism of infants also contains a prayer of exorcism.

Fasting

is the activity whereby a person restricts the amount of food eaten to only one full meal per day. It can be in the context of a special time in that person's life, perhaps a retreat or an intense period of prayer. The Church requires all adult members in good health to fast on Good Friday as a penitential action and invites this fasting to continue into the day on Holy Saturday as a joyful preparation for the celebration of Easter.

Inquirer

describes a person in the first stage of the process of Christian initiation.

Lectionary

is the ritual book which contains the Scripture selections to be read at Mass, both weekday and Sunday celebrations, arranged in accordance with the liturgical seasons*. The Lectionary, as revised by the Second Vatican Council, offers three readings for Sundays along with a Psalm text. The First Reading is usually from the Old Testament, the Second Reading is taken from a non-gospel New Testament text, and the Third Reading is taken from one of the Gospel accounts. A three-year cycle apportions out each of the synoptic Gospels over the course of the Sundays of that year. John's Gospel is read at Easter, on special feasts, and fills in on the year given over to Mark.

Liturgical Season

refers to the various periods of time in the Church calendar which are annually celebrated. There are five such seasons: Advent, Christmas, Lent, Easter, and Ordinary Time. Through the unfolding of this annual cycle of seasons, the Church celebrates the Paschal Mystery* of Jesus Christ. Thus, the very passage of time itself becomes a holy observance.

Liturgy

from Greek, *leitourgia*, "public works," denotes the communal, public and official worship of the Church contained in texts and rites* celebrated by the people of God when they gather. As the original Greek suggests, this activity is the work of the whole Church and does not lie with any one person or group. The entire household of the faithful does the liturgy and in so doing directs itself to the praise and glory of God.

Meditation

is a particular form of prayer whereby one purposely focuses attention. This focus may be achieved by concentrating on a singular image or object. Suitable objects for Christian meditation include texts of Sacred Scripture, religious artwork, events in the life of Christ, images of Mary and the Saints, and events of everyday life which heighten one's awareness of God.

Monasticism

derives from Greek, *monos*, or "one, alone," describing the institutional pursuit of religious life where individuals take vows of poverty, chastity, and obedience, separating themselves from the world either alone (as hermits) or in community. Monasticism attempts under the guidance of a rule (for example, the Rule of St. Benedict) to establish a life of prayer and work for the glory of God, for the personal holiness of the individual, and for the good of the Church and the world. Different monastic orders sometimes take their name from the founder of their rule, such as the Benedictines (St. Benedict), Franciscans (St. Francis of Assisi), and Dominicans (St. Dominic).

Neophyte

from Greek, *neophutos*, or "new plant, new growth," this term refers to those newly initiated who have celebrated Baptism, Confirmation and Eucharist. Neophytes, the newly initiated, are grafted onto Christ as vines to the branch and are so designated up until the first anniversary of their initiation.

Paschal Mystery

is the term encompassing Jesus' suffering, Death, burial, Resurrection, Ascension, and sending of the Holy Spirit. It refers to the saving activity of Jesus by which we are redeemed and given new life by the gracious love of God.

Purification and Enlightenment

is the third stage of Christian initiation. It begins on the First Sunday of Lent and concludes on Holy Saturday as the Easter Vigil commences.

Reflection

is similar to meditation but not as intense an activity. In reflection, one concentrates mental activity and takes the time and effort to carefully consider.

Rite

describes ceremonial activity that proceeds from specific liturgical rules or directions. Some examples are the Rite of Infant Baptism, the Rite of Christian Initiation of Adults, and the Rite of Anointing and Pastoral Care of the Sick. Not only these ritual books but all of the rites currently in use by the Church were revised at the direction of the Second Vatican Council.

Rite of Christian Initiation of Adults (RCIA)

is the ritual book in which the Church describes the formation process of Christian initiation. The Second Vatican Council called for the restoration of the ancient process of initiation which included stages of growth and conversion in Christ marked by steps or liturgical celebrations. The four stages in initiation are: Inquiry, Catechumenate, Purification and Enlightenment, and Mystagogy. The Rite of Acceptance into the Order of Catechumens is the step between Inquiry and the Catechumenate. The Rite of Election is the step which celebrates the beginning of Purification and Enlightenment. And celebrating initiation (Baptism, Confirmation and Eucharist) signals the step into Mystagogy.

Sacrament

from Latin, *sacramentum*, or "oath, pledge," which originally meant the oath taken by soldiers and office holders of the Roman Empire, but became the term used by the Church to indicate its seven foremost ritual celebrations. The Seven Sacraments are: Baptism, Confirmation, Eucharist, Marriage, Holy Orders, Penance and Reconciliation, and Anointing of the Sick. In these Seven Sacraments, God's love is expressed and grace is communicated. The saving life, Death, and Resurrection of Jesus (Paschal Mystery*) is the foundation and basis for the Seven Sacraments celebrated by the Church.

Sacramentals

are sacred signs instituted by the Church which, while they do not bear the same impact as the Seven Sacraments, nonetheless dispose people to holiness and an openness to God's grace imparted and experienced in the Seven Sacraments. Examples of sacramentals include blessings, exorcisms, and the use of holy water, rosaries, and sacred images in prayer.

Scrutiny

is the name given to the ritual celebrations occurring on the Third, Fourth, and Fifth Sundays of Lent during the stage of initiation known as Purification and Enlightenment*. Within the Scrutiny celebrations, a laying on of hands and an exorcism* prayer expresses the Church's concern for the elect*, as the community of the faithful prays that not only the elect but all of God's children be delivered from the power of evil.

Sponsor

describes the ministry of spiritual companion to a catechumen as he or she moves through the various stages of the initiation process up to the celebration of the Rite of Election when the person is then accompanied by a "Godparent." A baptized candidate* is accompanied by a sponsor throughout the whole initiation process.

Tradition

describes the living reality by which all of the Church's beliefs expressed doctrinally, its sacred writings expressed in scripture, and its prayer expressed in rituals are handed down and transmitted from one generation to the next under the guidance of the Holy Spirit. The Second Vatican Council articulated an understanding of tradition as the whole life and activity of the Church which helps men and women to be holy in this world. It is the totality of God's Revelation preserved and cherished by the household of the faithful.

Notes

Notes